7-13-56

*Complete Book of*

# The
# Wild Turkey

# COMPLETE BOOK OF THE

# Wild Turkey

## ROGER M. LATHAM

*Illustrated by Ned Smith*

THE STACKPOLE COMPANY
HARRISBURG, PENNSYLVANIA

# DEDICATION

This book is dedicated to those still living who pioneered in wild turkey management in my own State. Through their untiring efforts, this grand game bird was literally snatched from near extirpation and started on the road to abundance. Today, Pennsylvania is recognized as one of the leading wild turkey states in the country.

For their part in this magnificent job of conservation and restoration, my hat is off to Leon Keiser, Orrie Smith, Seth Gordon, William G. Fluke, Ross Metz, and Elmer Alexander. There are others who contributed a lot in time, effort, and knowledge, but these six are especially deserving of recognition.

# CONTENTS

CHAPTER 5

NATURAL ENEMIES AND OTHER LIMITING

# PART II. MANAGEMENT OF THE WILD TURKEY IN THE UNITED STATES

CHAPTER 6

CHAPTER 7

PAST AND PRESENT MANAGEMENT PRACTICES

# PART III. HUNTING THE WILD TURKEY

## CHAPTER 8

## CHAPTER 9

# PREFACE

At long last the native North American wild turkey is again coming into its own!

The pride and sustenance of our Pilgrim Fathers, long the accepted symbol of our annual Thanksgiving feast, has been the one most neglected important game bird on the Continent.

Had Ben Franklin's proposal prevailed, and the wild turkey (instead of the bald eagle) been used on the Great Seal of the new Nation to symbolize our liberty and independence, this grand game bird of forest and glade would undoubtedly have been idolized and restored to abundance long ago.

Instead, through lack of appreciation and neglect, the wild turkey was allowed to disappear over vast stretches of its ancestral ranges. In a few areas very limited numbers of turkeys survived solely through their ability to elude their enemies, including man.

Now, after a long, uphill struggle, led by a handful of pioneer workers, the wild turkey is staging a promising comeback! A goodly number of states are giving turkey restoration programs special attention, and the future prospects are most encouraging.

The writer proudly claims a small place in the ranks of the pioneers who helped to restore turkey hunting. No accomplishment during his more than forty years in the conservation field gives him more real satisfaction than the part he played in bringing back good turkey hunting to his native state of Pennsylvania.

Incidentally, he also nostalgically recalls the days when, as a mere youngster in kneepants, these big game birds each autumn scared the wits out of him by regularly making their hasty departure from beneath the same chestnut trees where he went to gather the delicious brown nuts.

Then all of a sudden both the wild turkeys and the chestnuts were gone, the turkeys from overshooting, the chestnut trees killed by a devastating blight.

He also vividly recalls the disappointing early efforts to bring back wild turkey hunting to that state, in which he participated some two decades later—the absolute closures of the hunting season for the birds; the purchase of many hundreds of hybrids (domestic and wild stock crossed) culled out of flocks on their way to market from the mountains of Maryland and West Virginia, which were temporarily penned and released on shot-out ranges in the hope of again starting wild breeding flocks; the early attempts to raise turkeys on state game farms suitable for release.

It is with pride, therefore, that he hails Roger Latham's book as the dawn of a new era in wild turkey restoration. This book is far more than a treatise on the best ways to outwit this most challenging creature of forest, swamp, and open glade. It is a unique handbook for both the sportsman and the wildlife manager, and should hasten the return of wild turkey hunting to millions of acres now devoid of turkeys.

Being divided into three major parts dealing with the history of the wild turkey, its management, and how to hunt them, any sportsman can use its detailed and authentic information to excellent advantage.

The reader will quickly learn that the genuine wild turkey is a "choosy" creature, quite specific in its habitat demands; that its eyesight and hearing are *far more* keen than those of most other birds and mammals, and therefore is not easily bagged by the uninformed novice; and, lastly, that the losses to predators during the nesting season, and from unfavorable weather conditions immediately after the young poults are hatched, far exceed the estimates commonly made by untrained observers.

Latham's discussion of the predator problem is one of the soundest this writer has yet seen, and he has been a close student of the subject for many years. The basic facts and theories presented can be relied upon—but unfortunately the average hunter just won't believe them.

Observing the ethics of the sport constitutes a major part of the real joy derived from any hunt, and especially when in pursuit of the wily turkey. The hunting advice, and how to use calls, are both exceptionally well done. And his safety warnings are most timely. Untrained turkey hunters scare more turkeys out of the country than a herd of elephants. And that goes for deer hunters, too. Why must men barge through the forest as though their sole mission is to spoil everybody's sport?

This book covers all the sportsmenlike hunting techniques with which I am acquainted, except one. And that's to "act like a turkey". Some years ago one of my old wardens, who had lived among the wild turkeys for over sixty years, told me about one of his experiences worth repeating.

It seems an albino turkey hen ranged widely on the mountain back of his farm which all the nimrods in the valley repeatedly tried to bag. She was not only an exceptional prize, but they sought to remove her lest she produce more albinos.

But this particular old hen turkey had become much wiser than her pursuers. She would respond to the call, but never came within gunshot.

Finally this old warden outwitted her by hiding back of a big log, long before daylight, in the area where she regularly fed. Then instead of calling, and he was an expert with his own throat, he merely scratched lightly in the leaves occasionally. Between well spaced "scratches" he remained absolutely still. When the white hen came within hearing she began working toward the watchful hunter, who merely imitated the feeding noises of another wild turkey. And thus he bagged the elusive snow-white prize.

Yes, as Latham says, "If you want to bag a wise old wild turkey you must be smarter than the turkey."

Now a word about the author: Roger Latham literally grew up with a gun in his hand, a bunch of traps over his back, and a dog by his side. He entered the Pennsylvania Game Commission's training school by competitive examination, and graduated with flying colors. Instead of being assigned to a law enforcement job, he was detailed to the Division of Research. There he handled numerous difficult assignments, all of them well.

Then he decided that he could do his job better if he had a college education. He obtained leave, and struggled through the task of keeping the family together while he completed five years of college.

During those five tough years he continued to live in the outdoors, studying wildlife. Upon graduation he returned to his old love, the Research Division of the Pennsylvania Game Commission, this time as its head.

Roger Latham is a fine sportsman first, a clear-headed scientist second. He is an exceptionally keen and impartial field observer. Roger has literally "slept with the wild turkeys" and their problems for weeks on end. I know of no one else so well equipped to write such a book.

May this excellent volume hasten the restoration of wild turkey hunting, one of the grandest sports I know, throughout the land; and may you, the reader, derive much more genuine pleasure from your turkey shooting in the future.

SETH GORDON

Sacramento, California

# INTRODUCTION

This book is written about the largest, the most intelligent, and the most prized upland game bird on the North American continent—the wild turkey. The wild turkey is more than just another game bird. It serves as a symbol of a new American philosophy. Through ruthless slaughter and complete disregard for conservation principles, this bird was reduced to a point near extermination. Then, with a feeling of shame and remorse at this near catastrophe, the people of the United States resolved to right this and other wrongs perpetrated against our wildlife, our forests, our soils, and our waters. With perseverance and determination they are accomplishing this task. The wild turkey has been saved and is rapidly being restored to a large part of its former range. This successful restoration program proves that civilized man *can* live in harmony with Nature.

The writings contained herein are divided into three parts. The first part is about the bird itself. A brief history of the wild turkey in North America is presented showing its original range and how it was reduced from great numbers over a vast area to a mere token population in a few isolated spots. A general description is given of the bird's distinguishing characteristics and of the various sex and age differences. Its life history and habits, its habitat requirements, and the role of predators and other limiting factors in its struggle for existence are included.

Part two concerns the management of the wild turkey in North America. The Pennsylvania story is told to illustrate the possibilities of restoration in areas where the wild turkey was extirpated at least a half century earlier. It explains how hunting restrictions contribute to the conservation of the species, and how game refuges and predator control may be of value under certain conditions. The subject of stocking artificially reared wild turkeys is discussed, and both sides of this controversial question is presented. It explains how forest lands have been managed successfully for wild turkeys in many parts of the country—how artificial and natural foods can be produced and which ones are best suited for this purpose. The importance of forest openings or field edges is stressed. These grassy areas produce the large quantities of insects and green forage necessary for the growth and health of young poults. Without them a forest is much less likely to support a satisfactory number of birds. And finally, the need for emergency winter feeding is treated.

The third and final portion of the book is devoted to the art of hunting the wild turkey. The hunter is told what equipment to use—the kind of rifle or shotgun and the proper ammunition. The various callers are described in detail and the reader is shown how to make several good ones at home. Turkey behavior in the woods is explained thoroughly, and the hunter is told what he must do to outwit his wily quarry. He is told how to call turkeys—what notes to imitate and when. And he is offered a course in "still hunting." Although many things can only be learned by experience, it is believed that this book provides most of the fundamentals required for successful hunting.

The book is written primarily for the sportsman. The early history is given because it should be of interest to him. The discussion of the bird's life history and habits provides the background so essential to success in his sport. The management section is for the guidance of the individual sportsman or the sportsmen's club. For those who want to introduce wild turkeys on their own lands or for those who want to improve their hunting, the management outline should be helpful. It is hoped that state conservation departments and state game commissions will also find it useful. Every attempt has been made to give the sportsman all of the information he will need to become a real honest-to-goodness turkey hunter. It is intended to save him the trouble of learning many things "the hard way."

To the writer's knowledge, only three other wild turkey books have been published. *The Wild Turkey in Virginia* by Henry S. Mosby and Charles O. Handley is a semi-technical work published by the Virginia Commission of Game and Inland Fisheries, Richmond. This work is a report of extensive studies and deals mainly with the status, life history, and management of the bird in the Commonwealth. Only a few pages are devoted to hunting methods. The second, *The American Wild Turkey* by Henry E. Davis published by Samworth, is a book written for hunters. The locale of the book is South Carolina, and the hunting experiences described are mainly for that state. The third, *The Wild Turkey and Its Hunting* by Edward A. McIlhenny published by Doubleday, Page and Company, is also a turkey hunter's book. Mr. McIlhenny pursued his sport in the states bordering the Gulf of Mexico, and this is the type hunting he describes. Except for a turkey calling and hunting manual put out by Tom Turpin in Memphis, Tennessee, this is the extent of the literature devoted solely to this grand game bird.

This is the first book about the wild turkey written with a northern accent. Although turkeys and turkey hunting country-wide are treated in this work, emphasis is placed upon the bird and its hunting in the northern states. Particular emphasis is given to management problems in colder climates. For this reason, it is expected that this book will especially appeal to sportsmen in the more northern states where the wild turkey has been reintroduced within the past few years. It is hoped that these pages will give these nimrods a greater appreciation of the efforts being made by the state conservation commissions or departments, and provide the essentials for them to realize the greatest possible recreation when these efforts bear fruit.

# PART 1
## ABOUT THE WILD TURKEY ITSELF

FROM FOSSIL evidence found in rocks and caves, we know that the wild turkey roamed the primeval forests of America many thousands of years before Columbus made his epic journey to the New World. As many as five different prehistoric turkeys have been described, but how many actually existed is much a matter of conjecture. Surely the present-day hunter is far more interested in the historic record anyway, and any detailed account of these prehistoric forms would be superfluous.

At the present time, there are six recognized races of the wild turkey, Genus *Meleagris*, in North America. The original range of these various subspecies was as follows: The Eastern wild turkey (*Meleagris gallopavo silvestris* Vieillot) formerly occupied the entire area from southern Maine and Ontario south to Florida, west to Texas, and northward through Nebraska to South Dakota. Next westward was the Merriam turkey (*M. g. merriami* Nelson) which was found from Colorado to western Arizona and south into Mexico. From central Texas to Northern Mexico lived the Rio Grande turkey (*M. g. intermedia* Sennett). The Florida wild turkey (*M. g. osceola* Scott) is confined entirely to the peninsula of Florida. Two other races are found only in Mexico—the Mexican turkey (*M. g. gallopavo* Linne) from which the domestic turkey originated, and a subspecies (*M. g. onusta* Moore) still without a common name. A map showing the original range of these subspecies is given.

Another genus of turkeys is found in Yucatan and adjoining central American states. The genus is represented by the ocellated or Yucatan turkey (*Agriocharis ocellata*) and is the smallest and probably most beautiful of all wild turkeys.

The greatest difference between the various subspecies of *Meleagris* is in coloration. *Silvestris* differs from *osceola* only in the color pattern of the outer wing feathers (primaries). On *osceola* they are black with tiny broken bars of white which do not extend completely from the outer edge of the feather to the shaft. The tips of the tail feathers in *gallopavo* are white, and this intergrades through various shades of creamy light buff and light brown in *onusta*, *intermedia* and *merriami* to the dark chocolate brown of *silvestris*.

The Mexican turkey is the smallest of this genus. The Rio Grande and the unnamed *onusta* appear to be the largest, although the Eastern wild turkey may actually produce individual winners in the thirty pound plus class.

The scientific name comes from the Latin. *Meleagris* means guineafowl. *Gallopavo* is derived from *gallus*, a cock, and *pavo*, a peafowl.

# Chapter 1:

## From the Time of the Indians

THE ORIGIN of the domestic turkey is a fascinating bit of history. Even though the Eastern wild turkey was by far the most abundant and had the greatest range, its smaller cousin in Mexico was actually the progenitor of all present-day domestic strains. There is a simple explanation for this. The Aztec Indians of Mexico were a highly civilized race, living in permanent homes, and extensively cultivating the soil. On the other hand, the more nomadic Indians living within the confines of the Eastern wild turkey range had little reason or desire to domesticate these birds, because turkeys could be obtained in the wild in almost any quantity with a minimum of effort.

Thus, the domesticated stock originating from *Meleagris gallopavo gallopavo* was believed to have been transported back to Spain by Cortez following his explorations in Mexico. From Spain, they were introduced into the rest of Europe, and actually came back to North America with the early colonists. Over the years, however, much cross-breeding between this domestic bird and the Eastern wild turkeys (*meleagris gallopavo silvestris*) has probably resulted in a modern domestic turkey which contains blood from both subspecies.

The origin of the name "turkey" is somewhat obscure. One theory is that when this bird was originally introduced to Europe it was confused with the guineafowl (*Nunida meleagris*), and the name was applied to both birds for some time. Because the guinea was believed to have come from the region of Turkey, it was thought that both birds orig-

3

inated there. When finally the confusion was clarified, the guinea-fowl was given its present name and the turkey retained its common name.

Another suggestion advanced is that "turkey" was a mispronunciation of the Indian name for the bird, "furkee" or "firkee." And finally, there is the thought that the bird's call of "turk, turk" suggested its name. Most hunters and ornithologists question this theory, because the call notes do not actually reproduce this sound but rather a "keow, keow."

The Indians used thousands of these great birds for food, clothing, and in the construction of arrows, but strangely enough, there was a considerable difference of opinion concerning its food qualities among the different tribes. For example, the Apaches of the southwest frowned upon this bird and other wild fowl as food and preferred the red meat of big game animals. Even in the East, most tribes preferred fish to fowl. Among some tribes it was taboo to cook the meat of turkeys and deer in the same pot.

Among the Cherokees, only the children bothered to hunt turkeys during most of the year. The older, experienced hunters spent their time stalking more desirable prey. The eight- to ten-year olds killed them by blowing a dart through a hollow cane. They were sufficiently accurate with their crude weapon to hit most of their victims in the head, usually through the eye. Body shots would not have made a clean kill, if they killed at all.

This same tribe used a disguise made from the skins of turkeys to hunt them in the spring. This was also a sport for the boys. One would secrete himself behind a log, show a part of the turkey plumage, and call to the turkeys with

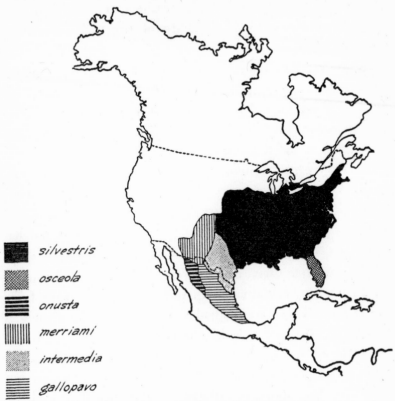

silvestris

osceola

onusta

merriami

intermedia

gallopavo

ORIGINAL DISTRIBUTION OF
RACES OF THE WILD TURKEY
(Meleagris gallopavo)

his voice. Evidently with proper technique, the unsuspecting birds would walk close enough to be grabbed around the feet with the bare hands, much like the falconer catches his live hawks today.

The Indian's arrows were fletched with the stiff primary feathers of the wing just as they are at the present time. Captain John Smith found that the Indians were also using the spurs as arrow points. They used various feathers in their ceremonial dress, including coats or mantles constructed entirely from the beautiful body feathers. The wild turkey contributed much to the welfare of the early American Indian.

At the time of colonization, wild turkeys were exceedingly abundant on the Eastern part of the continent from southern Maine and Ontario south to Florida and west into the Great Lakes region. The early settlers and explorers regularly mentioned the turkey in their journals and writings of the day. This magnificent bird formed an important part of their diet and was everywhere hunted by white and red men alike. Because wild turkey was perhaps the most conspicuous part of the first Thanksgiving feast, this bird has been associated with this holiday each year since.

Some of the early descriptions of turkeys and turkey abundance are very interesting. William Wood writing from Massachusetts about 1630 had this to say: "The Turkey is a very large Bird, of a blacke colour, yet white in flesh; much bigger than our English Turkey. He hath the use of his long legs so ready, that he can runne as fast as a Dogge, and flye as well as a Goose: of these sometimes there will be forty, threescore, and a hundred of a flocke, sometimes more and sometimes lesse; their feeding is Acorns, Hawes, and Berries, some of them get a haunt to frequent our English corne: In winter when the Snow covers the ground, they resort to the Sea shore to look for Shrimps, and such smal Fishes at low tides. Such as love Turkie hunting, must follow it in winter after a new falne Snow, when hee may follow them by their tracts; some have killed ten or a dozen in halfe a day; if they can be found towards an evening and watched where they peirch, if one comes about ten or eleven of the clocke he may shoote as often as he will, they will sit, unless they be slenderly wounded. These Turkies remaine all the yeare long, the price of a good Turkie cocke is foure shillings; and he is well worth it, for he may be in weight forty pounds."

One of the most interesting facts concerning the turkey during the early days was its comparative tameness or lack of fear of man. Evidently until the birds learned from constant persecution that man was their greatest enemy, they were relatively unsuspicious of him and would let a hunter approach within gunshot with little misgiving. How different they are today! But even now, one needs only to go into Central Canada to witness a similar phenomenon. Up there in the wilderness, a .22 pistol or rifle is more than an adequate weapon to pick off ruffed grouse sitting in the trees a few feet from the hunter. Some may actually be killed with clubs or slingshots. But a ten gauge magnum is hardly gun enough for some days in Pennsylvania!

It is difficult to determine sometimes the exact year when a bird finally disappears from an area. According to the best records, however, the wild turkey was gone in Minnesota by 1871, northern Indiana by 1870, southern Indiana by 1900, Michigan by 1886, and Wisconsin by 1872. Peculiarly enough, the last birds were recorded in Ontario as late as 1902.

Farther east the final dates varied considerably. They had disappeared from Connecticut by 1813, Vermont by 1842, Massachusetts by 1851, and Ohio by 1903. Out west, 1915 saw the end of the native turkey in Nebraska and 1920 ended its existence in South Dakota. By 1920, the wild turkey could no longer be found in 18 of the 38 states included in its original ancestral range.

Dr. C. H. D. Clarke of Toronto wrote an epitaph for Ontario turkeys which applies equally as well to these 18 states: "The curtain came down simultaneously on turkey and forest. The last bird may have been shot, but if he was, it was the axe and not the gun that made him the last."

# Chapter 2:

## General Description

*Conformation, Plumage, Markings, and Color*

MOST HUNTERS have a very good idea what a wild turkey looks like even if they have never seen one, because there is a marked likeness in general appearance between the wild bird and the domestic bronze. But there are important differences between the two, and every hunter should be able to recognize most of them. On occasion, this knowledge could save him some embarrassment if he happened to come across a flock of domestic birds which had strayed a little too far from the farmhouse! Then, too, he can call the bluff of the joker who returns home with a big gobbler he bought from some farmer's flock and claims that it is a genuine wild turkey from away back on the head of Laurel Run.

Most sportsmen are not interested in exhaustive descriptions of plumage, markings and color of game birds. If the individual is, he can find detailed descriptions in a number of bird books. Only the outstanding and important features will be given here — just enough so that the hunter will become better acquainted with the bird he will  eventually grow to admire and respect more than any other, if he has not already done so.

The Eastern wild turkey, generally speaking, is a slender-bodied, long-legged, long-necked and long-tailed bird with a tiny head. The more nearly it conforms to this description, the more nearly it approaches the standards of perfection set for the truly wild bird. With minor exceptions

9

WILD TURKEY                DOMESTIC TURKEY

these characteristics also apply to the western forms. The wild turkey should have slender, small-boned legs and a snake-like neck. Those conforming to the best type should present an appearance of super streamlining, tapering from the middle to almost nothing at the end of the tail and tip of the bill.

The wattles and caruncles of the gobbler should be small and comparatively inconspicuous. As the males become older, there will be some increase in size of these fleshy appendages, and during the breeding season they will also enlarge temporarily, but they should never resemble those of the domestic tom. The head should be flat, narrow and racy, with little or no forehead. The eyes are large.

With one exception, the wild bird should never have a heavy "dumpy" body. The slender body should taper both ways from the middle and not have the prominent breast of the domestic bird. The exception to this rule is the adult gobbler during the breeding season. At this period, the older tom has developed a cellular layer of fat over the breast and crop cavity. This "breast sponge" as it is called gives the breeding gobbler a rounded and protruding breast which temporarily deprives the bird of his streamlined appearance. The breast sponge is evidently a reservoir of energy which serves to tide the gobbler through the breeding season. Because he is exceedingly active at that period, he uses a large amount of energy. At the same time he has little time to feed, and quite often high-energy foods such as acorns and other mast crops are not available. The spring diet consists of much green forage, fleshy fruits, and miscellaneous insects, all of low caloric value. Thus, the breast sponge is used much as a hibernating animal uses its layer of fat during its long sleep. By the end of the breeding season, the gobbler's fat store is pretty well used, and he has again resumed his streamlined appearance.

Except for the minor differences in plumage coloration and markings noted earlier, there is little difference between the various sub-species of wild turkeys. However, the Eastern wild turkey differs from the domestic turkey in several ways. The tips of the tail coverts (rump feathers) are white in the domestic bird and cinnamon-brown in the wild bird. Also, the retrices (long tail feathers )are white-tipped in the barnyard fowl and chocolate-tipped in the native bird. But, it should be remembered that these feather tips are white to light buff in the Mexican turkey, the Merriam's turkey, and the Rio Grande turkey.

The body plumage also differs between the domestic and wild birds. The native bird has darker body feathers, and at some distance or in deep shade, a wild turkey will appear black. Its body plumage also has a metallic iridescence which is lacking in its barnyard counterpart. In sunlight and at different angles, its feathers may reflect various shades of red, bronze, blue, purple, green, and brown. It is these iridescent colors reflected in the sunlight which so delight the hunter and is just one more reason why the wild turkey is so popular with nimrods anywhere it occurs.

The color of the bare part of the head and neck of the wild turkey is a subject of much controversy. Some say it should be blue to conform to the standards of the genuine wild turkey. Others say some red is permitted or that the head can be almost all red at certain times and under certain conditions. The truth is that the color of the head may be altered at the will of the bird, or changes may come as a response to danger or other external stimuli. This latter response is probably caused by a release of adrenalin into the blood stream with a consequent redistribution of the blood in the body.

The bright blue of the turkey's head or neck is a pigment. The red color is caused by blood circulating just under the skin. During the gobbling season of spring, the wattles, including the teat-like frontal wattle on top of the head, become enlarged and may turn a crimson red. These changes apparently accompany the enlargement of the testes and the increased secretion of sex hormones into the blood. When a gobbler is strutting, the color of the top and sides of the head and the shape of the frontal wattle can be altered at will. A red crown may change to whitish blue during the strut and back to red again all in a few seconds. The frontal wattle may be red and erect one moment, and then blue and pendant the next.

The red coloration of the head and wattles of the breeding season is usually not lost until September when the gonads (testes) have again receded in size.

The major differences between the heads of wild and domestic birds are in the color and size and the development of the various fleshy or warty appendages. The wattles and caruncles of the tame turkey are much larger throughout, and the head retains the predominant red color the entire year. The young domestic males have these characteristics well developed during the first breeding season, whereas the young wild tom still resembles the female very closely in the appearance of the head. There is a much greater abundance of hair-like feathers on the head and necks of wild gobblers, particularly of the yearlings.

The feet and legs (tarsi) of the wild bird are normally some shade of pink except for the first year when they are more likely to be a mahogany brown or a grayish-brown with a tinge of dark red. In the domestic bird the feet and legs are black, purplish-black, dark gray, or dark red. On either type, the color of the legs may be modified when the scales become loosened prior to shedding. This adds a silvery gray cast over the underlying color.

Occasionally, totally white or partially albino wild turkeys are observed. In 1952 five albino wild birds were sighted in West Virginia in one group, and in the fall of 1953 a twenty-pound white gobbler was killed from a flock of five in the same vicinity. Presumably these were the same birds which had survived for at least a year and a half in spite of their color. Single observations are not too uncommon over most of the range.

### Sex and Age Differences

Wild turkeys can be sexed immediately following hatching by an examination of the genital papillae just within the external opening of the cloaca. This anal method is identical to that used for separating the sexes of day-old domestic chickens. This technique, originated by the Japanese, is now widely used in this country, and trained sexers can be found anywhere poultry is raised in quantity.

At about ten to twelve weeks of age, the hens and toms begin to show external sexual differences which will permit sorting. The heads and necks of the males show a greater area of nearly bare skin, usually pink and blue. These same sexual differences are even more pronounced in adult birds.

A hen of the year when killed in late fall should weigh eight to ten pounds and the young gobblers twelve to fourteen. Naturally, late hatched birds will weigh much less, and it is not too uncommon to see a brood in November in which the young birds will weigh as little as four to six pounds. The amount and quality of food available will have a considerable bearing on how fast the poults grow and how

## SEX DIFFERENCES

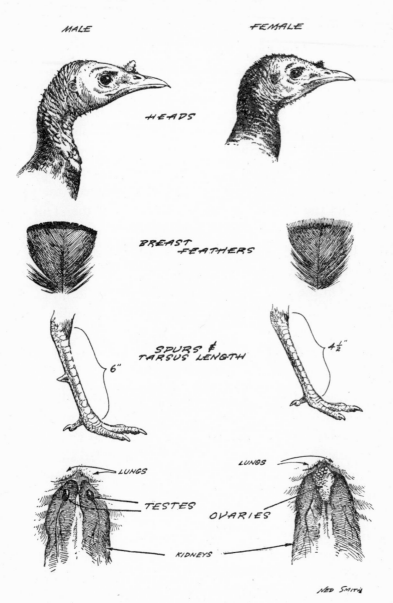

MALE

FEMALE

HEADS

BREAST FEATHERS

SPURS & TARSUS LENGTH

6"

4½"

LUNGS

LUNGS

TESTES

OVARIES

KIDNEYS

NED SMITH

fat they will be in the hunting season. Older birds show an even greater difference in weight. Adult hens will seldom exceed twelve to fourteen pounds, but older gobblers may on occasion go to twenty-five pounds or even more.

The tarsi (the bare part of the leg between the foot proper and the knee joint) averages about an inch and a half longer in adult males than in the hens, and is much heavier. This bone in the toms averages about 6½ inch in length, and about 5 inches in the hens. The foot and toes are much longer and larger throughout in the gobbler. A large gobbler track may measure as much as 6 inches between the tip of the hind toe and the tip of the middle front toe. This span in the adult hen is seldom more than 4½ inches.

The best and easiest method for distinguishing sex in the wild turkey is by examining a breast feather from adult birds. On the gobbler they are black-tipped and on the hen they are buff-tipped. By this method, sex can be determined at a glance because the hen's breast has a definite rusty wash while the male will be predominately black except for the iridescent reds and blues.

The adult female will be rather well feathered over her neck and head with short black bristles which give her an "unshaven" appearance. In the male, the head and neck are comparatively bare, and the warty caruncles and wattles are much more prominent than the tiny bluish bumps on the hen's neck.

The hen almost never grows spurs, but merely produces a tiny, rounded scale at the location where this growth occurs in the male. The gobbler-of-the-year shot in the fall will not have spurs either, but the rounded scale (button) will be much larger and will protrude just slightly.

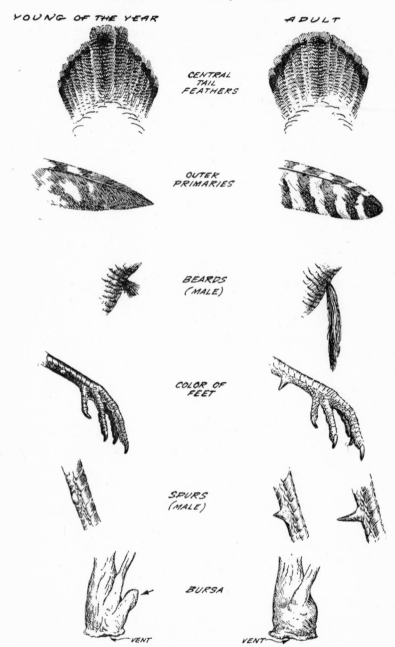

# AGE DIFFERENCES

YOUNG OF THE YEAR

ADULT

CENTRAL
TAIL
FEATHERS

OUTER
PRIMARIES

BEARDS
(MALE)

COLOR OF
FEET

SPURS
(MALE)

BURSA

VENT

VENT

Older gobblers will have obvious spurs usually a half-inch or more in length.

There is one final, positive method by which all birds can be readily sexed. All doubt can be dispelled by an internal examination. After the gizzard, liver, and intestines have been removed, the testes of the male or the egg cluster of the female can be located just at the front tip of the kidneys. The kidneys are the liver-red organs lying on both sides of the backbone in the rear part of the back. Just at the point where the back breaks naturally, the two white to gray, testes, as large as the end of a finger, will lie in each side of the backbone. The egg cluster, composed of many thousands of tiny eggs, is located in a median position directly over the backbone. Incidentally, all female birds are hatched with all of the eggs that they will ever lay already formed in their bodies.

To tell the age of a bird is also relatively simple, especially for distinguishing birds of the year from older birds. The young bird, which is usually shot in the fall when it is about six months old, has feet and legs which are mahogany brown to grayish-brown in color. Birds older than one year will have pink feet and legs, and the older the bird the deeper and more vivid the pink color becomes. This holds true for both sexes.

The young toms have only a slightly rounded button where the spur will be. Gobblers a year and a half old will usually have a blunt spur at least a half to three-quarters of an inch long, and older toms may have sharp spurs up to two or more inches in length. Young birds will most often have relatively sharp, pointed toenails, but older birds will have badly worn and blunted nails.

The beard can sometimes be used as a rough criterion of age. Gobblers of the year may have no beard at all, in the fall, and seldom one which protrudes beyond the breast feathers. Yearling toms rarely have beards more than five inches long and these are likely to be spread across the end like a loose whiskbroom. These will have a burned appearance as well. Gobblers with beards over eight inches long are likely to be three or more years old. These will be more uniform in diameter and color. However, beards may be deformed or worn, and are not a reliable designation of age. In fact occasionally a tom turkey is shot which may have more than one beard. Two or three beards are not extremely uncommon, and four and even five distinct, long beards have been reported on old gobblers.

Young turkeys molt three times before acquiring the full winter plumage. The first molt, called the postnatal molt, replaces the natal down and is complete except on the head and neck at six weeks. The head and neck has not lost this down until about the tenth or eleventh week. The second molt, the post juvenal molt, begins in about the fourth week and approaches full development at about fourteen weeks except on the head. At about the fifteenth week the third molt, called the first winter molt, begins with the dropping of the two central pairs of tail feathers. These new feathers usually attain a length considerably greater than the rest of the tail feathers which are retained from the post juvenal molt. Thus, the tail of the young turkey of the year when spread will reveal that the central pairs are longer than the rest. In the adult turkey the tail feathers will be approximately the same length and form an almost perfect fan when spread.

The stiff flight feathers attached from the wrist joint outward are called the primaries, and in the turkey there are ten in number. During the first winter molt all but the last two are shed. In the fall molt of the adult bird, *all* are replaced. So when the hunting season comes in late fall, the young birds of the year have two old feathers on the tip ends of their wings. Because these have been in use for several weeks, they are worn to a rather sharp point from rubbing through the vegetation. The older birds with new outer primaries will have rounded ends on these two feathers (see illustration). Also on the older birds these two feathers will likely have loose, silvery scales on the quill ends close to the point of entry into the flesh. The old feathers of the bird of the year will be shiny and polished in comparison. Just as an added note of interest, the young domestic turkey will replace all but the *last* primary at the first winter molt, so that this is another method of separating wild birds from domestic birds.

Wildlife technicians use still another method for aging turkeys. Just inside of the vent, and attached to the cloaca, is a pouch-like structure of lymphoid tissue called the bursa of Fabricius. This structure is lost at about eight months of age so that any bird still possessing it can be classified as a bird of the year. Technicians can determine the presence or absence of the bursa by probing from the outside with a suitable tool, or by dissecting a dead bird. This method is particularly useful for hens which are more difficult to age than gobblers.

### *Vocabulary*

The wild turkey is notably vocal. The most generally

known vocal effort is the rolling gobble of the tom during spring and summer as he sounds his defiance to other males and at the same time signals his presence to the fair ladies of his clan. This mating call is by no means confined to the breeding months alone, for it may be heard on occasion nearly anytime of the year. Sometimes it appears to be an involuntary response to a loud or unexpected noise. The distant report of a gun, the slamming of a car door, or the barking of a dog may elicit a quick gobble. Audubon mentions that they will answer the imitated hoot of the barred owl, and many were located and killed in this manner in his day. Of course, they will also answer the whoo whoo-hoo whoo-whoo of the horned owl.

Gobbling is ordinarily considered a function of the male turkey alone, but Audubon claims that hens over one year old will also strut and gobble just prior to the moment of mating. The author has never witnessed this performance in the breeding antics of captive birds, although it may occur in the wild.

Both sexes utter a variety of yelps, purrs, clucks, purts and other sounds with a variety of meanings. Most sounds are for communication, but some denote distress or alarm. These will be described in detail in the section of the book devoted to hunting. Because a close imitation of parts of these sounds are necessary for calling turkeys, and because the alarm notes must never be reproduced if success is to be attained, the detailed description of these vocal notes is left until later.

## Flight and Running Characteristics

Young turkey poults are first able to fly to any extent

when about four weeks of age. At that age they are capable of flying 25 to 50 feet, and may make it into the lower limbs of trees or shrubs to roost.

For a bird of its size, the adult wild turkey is exceedingly adroit on the wing. When frightened in thick cover, it can leave the ground almost as well as a grouse and be out of gunshot in no time at all. When leaving the ground, the bird takes a few fast running steps, a couple of hops, and is airborne. With powerful and rapid wingbeats, it may tower upward and clear the tallest trees or go slipping through the limbs and foliage almost as gracefully as the smaller forest-dwelling game birds. Once over the top or in the clear, the bird sets its wings and, except for an occasional wing beat, glides the rest of the way. While flying, the feet are extended beneath the tail and the neck is fully stretched forward.

When lighting on the ground, the bird throws its feet forward, stands on its tail in the air, and "back-pedals" with its wings. The tail is fully spread as a brake. When it touches the ground, the speed is only partly checked so that the bird must run rapidly for several yards before it comes to a full stop. When lighting on a limb, the body is pitched more steeply, and the reverse thrust of the wings is even more vigorous to bring the heavy body to an almost complete stop in midair.

When flushed, turkeys will usually fly from a quarter of a mile to a mile or more depending largely upon the kind of terrain. In flat country, the flights are likely to be comparatively short because of the effort required to keep aloft. Where a bird may leave the top or side of a mountain and glide "downhill," the flight may be much longer.

From the top or rim of a ridge, the turkey will usually head more or less straight down the sides for a couple hundred yards or so and then gradually swing out along the sides and finally come to rest somewhere half way down or lower.

Birds flushed repeatedly will soon tire and may eventually be unable to rise again. When fatigued, they will often hide in thick cover much like a pheasant, grouse, or quail and sometimes will not flush until almost tramped upon. Mosby and Handley tell of a nineteen pound gobbler in Virginia which finally landed in the Roanoke River after the third flush even though the river was only about one hundred yards wide at that point. One of the hunters retrieved it with a boat and it made little effort to escape. A fast dog can catch a turkey by flushing it repeatedly.

Turkeys have been "clocked" during flight a number of times, and these large birds are able to attain high speeds once underway. Three different Virginia birds were timed with a stop watch and found to be flying between 32 and 43 miles an hour. A North Carolina motorist raced a turkey for about a mile in his automobile and found that it held a uniform speed of 55 miles per hour. He kept the bird at top speed by blowing the horn. Downhill at full glide, the speed of this large bird may exceed this rate by a wide margin. A turkey traveling overhead at this speed is an almost impossible target for the gunner, unless he has had long experience in "pass shooting" waterfowl. Only ducks and doves ordinarily attain speeds like this. Compared to other common upland game birds, the turkey is among the fastest fliers. The ring-necked pheasant and the turkey attain about the same maximum speed, but both will outdistance ruffed grouse and bobwhite quail.

Young, lighter turkeys will take to wing as readily as a pheasant or grouse when alarmed, but the older heavier birds seem to prefer to run to escape man or other enemies. These big birds can fly well enough once airborne, but the energy required to get off the ground seems to discourage the effort. All pheasant hunters know how quickly a ringneck can disappear over the horizon once he has been knocked to the ground with a broken wing. A turkey can do it even better and faster under similar circumstances. Even the best athlete could not catch a wounded wild turkey in the forest. The strides of a large gobbler being chased by a dog were found to be three and one-half to four feet, in length, and it is claimed that a running turkey can keep in front of a galloping horse for short distances. Davis mentions an instance where a fox dashed into a flock of turkeys and was outrun for at least fifty yards until they took to wing. However, a fast dog can run down a winged turkey in thick cover.

## Swimming

Audubon in his incomparable "Ornithological Biography" tells how a flock of turkeys cross the larger rivers during their migratory movements to better feeding grounds. "At length, when the weather appears settled, and all around is quiet, the whole party mounts to the tops of the highest trees, whence, at a signal consisting of a single cluck, given by a leader, the flock takes flight for the opposite shore. The old and fat birds easily get over, even should the river be a mile in breadth; but the younger and less robust frequently fall into the water — not to be drowned, however, as might be imagined. They bring their wings close to their body, spread out their tail as a support, stretch forward their necks, and, striking out their legs with great vigour, proceed rapidly toward the shore; on approaching which, should they find it too steep for landing, they cease their exertions for a few moments, float down the stream until they come to an accessible part, and by a violent effort generally extricate themselves from the water."

Others have observed that the winged wild turkey will unhesitatingly take to water to escape a pursuing hunter or dog, even though the river or pond be a wide one.

## Longevity

In the wild it is difficult to ascertain the exact age of any game bird unless at some time it has been banded, either prior to release from a game farm or as the result of a live-trapping program. In heavily hunted states, these band returns are almost non-existent after the second or third year which indicates that the life expectancy is very short indeed. It must be remembered that in any wild game population which remains relatively stable year after year, there are almost exactly as many birds die each year as are born that year. Usually, 60 to 80 per cent of upland game birds killed by hunters during the fall hunting season are birds hatched during the past spring and summer — the young of the year. A large proportion of the remainder are about one and one-half years old. The number of adults two and one-half years old or more forms an almost insignificant part of the total. One possible exception to this rule comes during the low years of the grouse cycle, when survival of chicks may be so poor that the adult birds may actually outnumber the young in late fall.

In numerous instances, hunters report attempting to kill the same old gobbler in a particular area over a period of several years. The chance for error here is great, because one old gobbler could easily replace another which has been shot and carry on the legend indefinitely.

However, there have been several cases which appear to be authentic wherein the birds were believed to have reached an age of ten to twelve years and perhaps fifteen. It can be safely stated that any turkey which reaches his fifth year is an old-timer.

*Chapter 3:*

# Life History and Habits

## *Courtship and Mating*

ALL winter long, the turkeys have remained flocked, mostly in mixed family groups, but also in occasional bands of old bearded gobblers which seem to be too dignified to fraternize with such common turkeys as females and youngsters of the year. But the first warm days of late winter and early spring appear to cause an awakening of the mating instincts in the birds, and eventually the flocks break up into breeding harems. In this connection, I believe all hunters would be interested in knowing that the start of the breeding season is very little influenced by the coming of the warm spring weather. Actually, it is the lengthening of the days which produces this urge. Through receptive cells in the eyes, the increased amount of light causes a response from certain endocrine glands. The hormones produced under the stimulus of the light cause the testes of the male and ovaries of the hen to begin to enlarge. In the same manner, snowshoe hares, weasels, and ptarmigan turn from brown to white and back to brown as the amount of daylight decreases and then again increases. Wild turkeys and other birds would actually breed at about the usual date even though the temperature remained below freezing in the same way that a snowshoe hare can be made to turn white in midsummer heat by placing it in a darkened room.

The time of flock breakup and mating varies somewhat according to latitude. Florida or Georgia turkeys may start their breeding activities as early as February but Pennsylvania birds may not become interested before March or early April, especially during years when the late winter and early spring has been characterized by a lot of dark, cloudy days.

Unlike humans, where it is customary for the male to chase the female (?), the old tom establishes a gobbling point in the vicinity where he knows several hens are living and proceeds to call them to him. And they come willingly! Gobbling is influenced by weather, particularly in the very early spring, and the toms may stop entirely for a few days if the temperature drops markedly.

Gobbling usually starts just at daybreak and coincides closely with the first crow calls of the day. The gil-obble-obble-obble reverberates from mountain to mountain and may easily be heard for one or two miles on a quiet morning. Early in the spring, he may stop his calling within the first hour after sunrise, but, at the height of the season, the more amorous may continue to strut and gobble until late morning or even at intervals throughout the day.

In the wild, and even among captive turkeys, a certain amount of fighting between the  males  accompanies  the breeding season. This is apparently nature's way of assuring reproduction by the largest, strongest, and hardiest individuals. Some of the earlier fighting seems to be associated with the struggle for control of a certain territory, but later most of the combat results from a defense of the harem or individual hens within the harem. Most of these battles are brief and bloodless, although Audubon and a few others have reported fights to the death. Usually a weaker gobbler recognizes superior size and strength very quickly and retires from the field of combat. This supremacy of one gobbler over another is termed a "peck order" in wildlife parlance. Thus, a big gobbler three or four years old may beat one only two years old, and this one in turn will be able to drive off most yearlings. For this reason, few yearling gobblers ever have the opportunity to breed in the wild, simply because they are discouraged at every turn by older males.

Quite often young toms will attach themselves to a harem bossed by an older turkey and live in complete harmony so long as they show no tendency to mate. At the game farm, yearling males are capable breeders when isolated from older gobblers, although fertility normally averages somewhat lower.

One of the most fascinating spectacles a hunter can be privileged to see is a bearded old gobbler performing his courtship dance. It is surely one of Nature's most colorful pageants. He may be seen along the edge of some field or in some forest glade strutting before a lady fair who most of the time appears completely indifferent to his remarkable performance and glorious coloration. With the tips of his wings tight against the ground, his tail fully fanned and held perpendicular, and his neck arched so that his head presses tightly against his tail feathers, he walks sedately with slow and measured steps toward the hen. When almost to her, he takes several short, rapid steps, drags his quivering primaries over the ground which produces a sound much like that of sweeping the bare earth with a stiff broom, and completes the ceremony by gobbling. Associated with the strutting is a deep, throaty "humump" called a "pulmonic puff" by Audubon, which is emitted when his wings first touch the ground and he takes his first step. It has also been described as resembling the first wing-beat note of the drumming ruffed grouse.

Apparently with very few exceptions, the hens go to the gobbling male, and he seldom has to seek out a bashful member of the opposite sex. However, with the proper technique it is possible to lure a gobbler from his strutting grounds during the spring hunting seasons in some southern states. Hens will associate with the tom while he is displaying his courtship antics for some time before they are receptive to his caress. But once a receptive hen does appear, gobbling ceases at least until the business at hand is finished. These interruptions may last for fifteen minutes to a half hour or more.

As you have guessed by now, the turkey tom is polygamous and will mate with a number of hens. In the pens at a game farm, one male may sucessfully fertilize the eggs of as many as twenty to thirty hens. One mating is usually sufficient to fertilize an entire clutch of eggs, normally about fifteen, but wild hens will visit the gobbler almost daily during the laying period. If the hen has her first nest destroyed and she attempts to renest, then she will return to the gobbler for a second series of matings. This renesting, so common among all game birds, extends the breeding season over a period of about three months in the wild.

Early in the mating season, the hens may spend a large part of the day with their master. However, as egg-laying begins and progresses, they remain with him for shorter and shorter periods of time. The older hens appear to leave the mating group first. After incubation is well started, they no longer visit him at all and appear to try to avoid him as much as possible. Once deserted, he calls repeatedly for a week or two in a vain attempt to coax them back to him, but finally ceases his efforts entirely and joins with other lonesome gobblers for the remainder of the summer or perhaps even until the following spring.

## Nesting

The wild turkey hen may place her nest in almost any location, but the great majority are located near or even in forest openings. This is believed to be done deliberately, because the great bulk of the food of growing poults is secured from open areas in the form of insects and green forage. Within the deep forest, a hen would have difficulty finding sufficient high protein food to keep her hungry brood growing at a good rate. The nest itself may be placed almost anywhere, but there are certain definite tendencies. Most often it is made under some form of low concealing vegetation, such as a low-growing evergreen, a grape tangle, a fallen tree, a honeysuckle or greenbrier tangle, or other good cover. Sometimes where thick cover is scarce, the nest may be placed at the base of a good-sized tree, but this is seldom by choice. A wild turkey nest is a crude affair, being formed by the weight of the hen's body as she twists and wiggles her breast into the leaf or grass litter. These shallow depressions measure about eight by ten inches.

Egg laying begins about early to mid-April in northern states and about three weeks earlier in the extreme southern states. After some irregularity during the first few days, the hen will lay one egg per day until her clutch is completed. She lays about one hour later each successive day until the hour approaches too close to sunset when she will skip a day and resume laying early the following morning. The wild turkey egg is almost white to pale cream-buff and splotched to a greater or lesser extent with reddish-brown blotches. Some have practically none of these colored spots while others may be almost covered with them. The pattern will remain almost constant for the individual hen. The egg measures slightly less than two by two and one-half inches, which is somewhat larger than a good-sized chicken egg, but wider and not so long in proportion.

The average clutch size was found to be about 13 in Pennsylvania, 11 in Missouri, 11 to 12 in Virginia. The laying period occupies about 15 to 20 days depending upon the total number of eggs produced. Sometimes, particularly among spring-released game farm stock, two or more hens may lay in one nest and as high as forty eggs or more have been reported. Most often these multiple-hen nests are a failure.

There is a common belief, started by Audubon, that the gobbler will destroy every turkey nest he finds for the purpose of "protracting his sexual enjoyments." Little credence can be given this supposition. However, apparently a gobbler will attempt to tread a setting hen and may break some or all of her eggs in the process. This apparently is a rare incident.

Incubation requires twenty-eight days. During the early part of incubation, the hen will usually leave the nest for a short period each day to feed and drink, but as the hatching time approaches, she will sit tight for the last several days. When leaving her nest of her own accord, she carefully covers her eggs with leaves picked up by her bill. Some hens have a cute trick of carefully placing a large number of leaves on their backs as they sit patiently on the nest, and thus automatically cover the eggs when they slide out from under them.

During the early stages of incubation, the hen will desert her nest very readily if disturbed by predator or man. This proclivity toward desertion appears to be very much an individual characteristic. However, there is a pronounced difference among hens. Some hens will never return to a nest if they are flushed from it a single time by a human, while others will tolerate much disturbance. When hatching time approaches, almost all hens will permit a person to approach very closely before flushing. Audubon mentions building an enclosure around a wild hen for the purpose of catching her and her brood without frightening her away, but wild turkeys were not so wild in those days as they are at present.

Hatching covers a twenty-four to thirty-six hour period. Ordinarily in the wild, fertility of eggs is either one hundred per cent or zero. This means that the brood size upon hatching comes close to being the same as the clutch size. If the nest is approached during the hatching period, the hen ruffles her feathers and hisses loudly to warn off the intruder and will desert her babies only under extreme pressure. If the hatch comes off in a rain, she will ordinarily stay on the nest with her charges under her wings until the weather clears.

## The Brood

The hen takes her offspring away from the nest very shortly after they are dry, and leads them to the nearest field or forest opening where they can secure insects for their first meals. At first she must be extremely cautious with her brood, because the young wild turkey is very susceptible to exposure. For the first few days she must brood them each morning until the dew has dried from the vegetation before she dares move about with them. Any wetting, even from this source, on a day when the temperature is not high may mean the end of the poult. When it becomes wet and chilled, it will stop walking and sit in one place and peep pitifully. If it does not respond to its mother's call, it may be abandoned entirely, or she may return to it and brood the entire lot long enough to dry out the weakened poults. During periods of prolonged cold rains which may last for several days, entire broods are often lost because the hen eventually has to choose between losing them from starvation or exposure.

When a hen with young poults is approached, she will usually squat and "freeze." If discovered, or if suddenly surprised, the hen may feign a broken wing and attempt to lure the intruder away from her young. This defensive instinct is an admirable trait found in nearly all game birds, and undoubtedly is effective in saving a great many helpless chicks. Occasionally, the hen may attack an intruding human and flog him unmercifully.

The young turkeys spend each night on the ground under the mother hen's body and wings for the first four or five weeks. Then they begin to fly up with her, but may still crowd close to her on the limb. Toward late summer, two, three, or more hens may join together with their respective broods, and it is not uncommon to flush as many as fifty or sixty birds in a single flock. The difference in the size of the poults makes it obvious that there has been a banding together. These large groups may stay together until fall when there seems to be a tendency to split into smaller flocks. However, family ties seem to be strong and most of a hen's offspring are likely to stay with her even through the winter.

There are many unexplained behaviorisms in connection with wild turkey flocking habits. Certain patterns of flocking seem to be fairly constant, but there seem to be exceptions to all rules. Following the gobbling season, the males usually flock together until the brooding and rearing season is completed in late summer or early fall. Hens with their broods will join into large flocks, and these may remain intact until late summer or early fall. Then during the "fall shuffle" these family flocks seem to split off into smaller groups and may be joined by older gobblers so that by November the typical turkey flock may be composed of everything from young of the year to old bearded gobblers. Yet frequently, the hunter will encounter small bands composed entirely of old bearded gobblers. Why these old patriarchs insist upon this bachelor's existence, while others seem to prefer the company of the hens and their young, is not known. It is probably partly a matter of age, but evidently not entirely so.

During periods of stress in mid-winter when snows may be deep and food scarce in the more northern states, two or three flocks may join into a loosely associated group in the vicinity of some especially good source of food. This could be a grape tangle with a supply of dried fruit still clinging to the vines or perhaps a source of artificial feed such as is provided for them in Pennsylvania and other of the colder states. Sometimes as many as seventy-five or a hundred or more may come at one time to a single feeder filled with ear corn. As soon as the snow melts and the birds can again scratch through to the forest floor, this association quickly ends and each individual flock appears to return to its original home range.

The hunting season often has a decided influence on the ultimate composition of a wintering flock. When repeatedly scattered, there is no assurance that the family flock can ever reassemble completely, nor that remnants from heavily shot flocks will not join with it. Thus, like bobwhite quail, an original family unit may be dispersed to three or four other flocks by the time the hunting season is over in the fall. Of course, it is this tendency toward gregariousness that makes calling such an effective way of hunting wild turkeys. Except for the occasional old, nasty-dispositioned gobbler who, like Garbo, wants to be alone, most turkeys get lonesome very quickly and will respond readily to the invitation to join with others.

Adult wild turkeys roost in trees. In northern states, most often this is in hardwoods, but in southern states they may more often choose pines where available. Southern swampland birds have a propensity toward trees growing in water for roosting sites, and cypress and tupelo commonly serve for this purpose.

*Chapter 4:*

## Habitat Requirements

BECAUSE originally the wild turkey was found from the Atlantic to the Rockies and from southern Canada deep into Mexico, it is obvious that this bird, through its various subspecies, is adaptable to a wide variety of range conditions. Some were found in the upper northern hardwood forests where extreme winter temperatures and deep snows provided an annual test of their hardiness and adaptability. Under opposite climatic conditions there are birds which live in some of the near sub-tropical regions of Mexico, Florida, and other of our southern states. From East to West there were wide variations in total moisture—from the moist forests in eastern states to the arid regions of the West. Many were found in the flat pine country and the cypress swamps of the South where the highest elevations were often no more than a few feet above sea level. In contrast, much of the best range farther north was in the rugged Appalachians which often towered between two thousand and five thousand feet.

Only one requirement seemed to be reasonably constant throughout. Most of the turkeys occupied either mature or nearly mature forests. Nowhere were they brush birds as many of the grouse and quail are. It appeared that they needed and wanted large trees which were a dependable source of mast foods, and which provided safe roosting sites some distance from the ground. Also, because the wild turkey relies more upon its eyesight than anything else for security, they are definitely more vulnerable in thick cover to predators and man. They are even handicapped in their running and flying when brush is thick, and are much more comfortable in the more open, park-like stands of large timber. The fact that almost all of their range was clothed with mature forests before colonization probably accounts for the tremendous numbers of this bird at that time. In that same vein of thought, it is presumed that the wild turkey may return to many parts of its former range as the forests are permitted to become of age. Experiences in Pennsylvania and other states would bear out this premise.

## Size of Range

The term "range size" as used here is intended to denote the minimum and optimum area necessary or desirable to maintain a shootable population. This will vary considerably with the amount of gun pressure and many other factors. It may be possible to hold a token number of birds even on a few hundred acres of good land if these are carefully managed and protected. However, an isolated area of this size would seldom permit shooting except on a very limited and strictly regulated basis.

The smallest management unit to be worthwhile for most private shooting preserves would be nearer five thousand to ten thousand acres. Again with protection and controlled shooting, these relatively small areas will function satisfactorily. So many factors enter into the successful establishment and maintenance of a wild turkey population on small areas, it is almost impossible to predict whether an introduction will be a success or not. This phase of management will be described in some detail in a later chapter.

For the average state game department, the minimum

range size for public shooting would probably be at least 15,000 acres, and the optimum would be nearer 50,000 acres. Of course, in many states the entire range might encompass several million acres and much of this might be contiguous. In Pennsylvania, for example, at least 95 per cent of the 13,000,000 acres of occupied habitat is sufficiently contiguous that birds could conceivably travel or spread throughout its full extent. Only a few isolated ridges in the southeastern corner of the State and the South Mountain region of south-central Pennsylvania, which is cut off from the main range by the broad Cumberland Valley, are truly isolated.

Throughout the Appalachian Mountain region, the feeding range of an individual flock appears to be between two and three miles. This would mean that the average flock would travel over an area of 8,000 to 18,000 acres. On long narrow ridges, flocks may feed as far as five to eight or more miles along the sides and tops, but the total acreage covered may not exceed the above estimates. The feeding area covered during food shortages is likely to be greater than during seasons when mast, such as acorns, is particularly abundant. Human disturbance, and even predator pressure, may sometimes be responsible for an enlarged cruising radius.

In some of the western states where the turkeys may occupy different ranges during the winter and during the summer, the total area utilized may be very large. The winter range of a flock in some parts of Texas, for example, may be no more than a radius of five miles, but during summer this same flock may spread out as much as 18 to 20 miles. For this reason, 30,000 to 50,000 acres may be needed in this state to support a permanent wild turkey population.

## Terrain

Terrain appears to be of little significance except as it may provide protection or comfort in one way or another. Just as many birds may be found in flat swampland in some areas as on steepsided mountains in others. Usually, however, extensive forests and unfarmed land is associated with rugged terrain or swampland, particularly in the eastern states. Otherwise it is likely to have been cleared for crop-land long ago.

High and steep mountains provide good protection for wild turkeys against their archenemy—man. In the first place, at least fifty per cent of modern day hunters do not have the strength or ambition to climb to the top of the larger ridges and mountains. Birds flushed from the tops or sides of mountains can quickly fly out of gun shot, and may glide for a mile or more before lighting again. This is extremely important for turkey survival in heavily hunted regions. Of course, the great swamps of the South offer a refuge even more effective against most all of its enemies.

On the northernmost fringes of the present wild turkey range, irregular terrain may be valuable for other purposes as well. During extremely cold weather, birds may find roosting sites in pines or hemlocks in some deep valley and escape some of the fury of storms and high winds. When snow is deep, steep sides facing the sun may melt bare days, or even weeks, before the level areas do. This means precious food when it is needed most. Also, a great variation in topography often means a greater variety of year-round foods. Many food producing shrubs and trees may grow on the winter side of the mountain which do not appear on the sun face or on the top. Open springs during periods of deep snow may be instrumental in saving the lives of suffering turkeys, because they will scratch among the gravel for green vegetation, crayfish, aquatic insects, and other food items. Indirectly, too, steep topography may save many mature mast producing trees far beyond their normal life expectancy, simply because the lumbermen cannot get to them easily or cheaply.

*Cover*

Cover ordinarily refers to the quantity and kinds of vegetation found on the land. In wildlife management, cover can occasionally be artificial as in the case of junk piles, tiles, old automobile bodies, etc., but this kind of cover management does not work for the wild turkey. So, cover in this case does mean the vegetation.

Cover varies from North to South and from East to West almost as much as terrain. But, there seems to be one nearly constant factor which has already been mentioned—mature, or nearly mature, timber. This cover seems to be best suited to the needs of the wild turkey when it is fairly open and park-like. Turkeys become more vulnerable to predators and man in thick brush where they cannot use their superb vision to best advantage. And, of course, young forests do not produce large quantities of winter foods in the form of nuts and dry fruits like older stands of timber will.

Many forest types are represented throughout the ranges of the various subspecies. In eastern United States, most of the occupied habitat is in hardwoods with oak predominating. However, the new range in northern Pennsylvania where wild turkey populations are very high is in the northern hardwood belt where little or no oak is found. The cover there is predominantly birch, beech, maple, and wild cherry. Mast crops are decidedly irregular and, even in the best years, the quantity of food produced is very low in comparison with the oak forests of the southern half of the State.

In the southeastern states, particularly the Carolinas, Georgia, Florida, and the states bordering the Gulf, more pine appears in the typical cover. Of course many cypress and cypress-tupelo swamps offer some of the best habitat, but often in conjunction with pine uplands. Pure or nearly pure stands of southern pine rarely produce high populations of turkeys unless well interspersed with openings which supply green vegetation, insects, and seeds for food.

Western habitat, particularly in the arid regions, may be largely confined to the bottomland along the rivers and streams where the only timber of any size grows. Much of the surrounding territory is likely to be covered with grass or scrubby woody growth. In California, introduced Merriam's turkeys in the central foothills seem to be succeeding best on live oak-grassland interspersions. As always, mature hardwood timber seems to be the real key to success.

Besides the important factors of age, and to a lesser extent of species composition, there are other requirements for high productivity or even survival. One of the most important of these is the necessity of well interspersed forest openings. Their greatest value appears to be for rearing young poults. The most essential food for growing poults appears to be insects. Evidently only insects offer food in sufficient quantity for the ravenous youngsters and still provide the high-protein nutrition necessary for rapid growth and resistance to diseases and parasites. Only in grassy, weedy openings are insects ordinarily available in quantity—particularly the great favorite, the grasshopper. The openings will regularly be used as nesting sites as well.

Wild turkey biologists agree that forest-openings should constitute at least 10 per cent of the total habitat, and as much as 50 per cent may be tolerated. These openings should be scattered so that every sizeable block of forest contains several. Natural openings can usually be improved by management measures.

It is best to have a diversity of forest types on any range and these should be well mixed. In rugged terrain this occurs naturally. The north slopes will produce different vegetation from the south slopes of ridges, and the valleys or ravines will support species not regularly found at high elevations and on drier sites. An interspersion of food-producing shrubs and vines is also good. In the East, these may be the various dogwoods, viburnums, greenbriers, grapes, hawthorns, etc. In the West, they may be manzanita, coffee-berry, cedar berries, prickly pear, apples, tassajillo and others.

### Water

Water is another essential of wild turkey range. Rarely in the East is water a limiting factor, even on small areas, because the region is generally blessed with adequate rainfall and an abundance of streams, lakes, and ponds. Occasionally during severe droughts, turkeys will find it necessary to move their home range from a dry section to the vicinity of some available body of water. Even then, a good source of water can always be reached within a few miles at most.

In the West, water is a very important limiting factor, not so much for drinking purposes alone, but because its presence or absence usually governs the suitability or non-suitability of the vegetative cover for turkeys. But a source of free surface water is often not present even in forests which would otherwise be habitable. "Gallinaceous guzzlers" have been used successfully in arid sections of the west for extending the quail range, and earthen reservoirs and concrete watering troughs have proved acceptable to wild turkeys. The "guzzler" is a concrete catch basin which collects rain, stores it underground and dispenses it slowly during dry weather. Installation of these devices proved that water was *the* limiting factor for quail over thousands of acres.

For the first few weeks, young poults can usually survive without any source of free water. The early morning dew, succulent vegetation, and soft-bodied insects provide them with sufficient moisture. However, during drought periods these sources may be inadequate.

### Food of the Wild Turkey

An intimate knowledge of the food habits of the wild turkey can be exceedingly important to successful turkey hunting. If a hunter knows what turkeys eat, which items of the diet are abundant during that particular season, and where these foods can be found, it greatly simplifies his task of locating a flock. Also, it can be useful knowledge in case he, as an individual hunter, wishes to plant food-producing shrubs or trees for turkeys as his contribution to the management of this bird.

The diet of the wild turkey in the more northern states seems to follow a rather definite seasonal pattern. During the winter, it is principally mast in the form of acorns, grapes, flowering dogwood, black gum, beechnuts, wild cherry, hackberry, and greenbrier.

The various nuts and dried fruits are usually found among the leaves and trash on the forest floor and are obtained by scratching among this litter. Some forms of mast, such as grape and greenbrier, may remain attached to the stem throughout at least a part of the winter and be obtainable above ground. Other forms of mast which may form an important part of the winter diet in some areas are seeds of weeds and grasses, and cultivated grains. Almost anywhere green forage constitutes an important food item when available. Additional items, including animal life, may be gleaned from the unfrozen water of springs and streams.

Obviously the winter foods and food habits of wild turkeys in Florida and other warm areas would not be so markedly seasonal as in northern states. Where seasonal fluctuations in temperature and weather conditions are comparatively mild, the diet will tend to be more uniform throughout the year. On the other hand, on the northern fringe of the turkey range, deep snows may make mast foods almost completely unobtainable to the birds, and they may suffer considerable weight losses on substitute foods of poor quality (buds, etc.) until the snows again melt.

Spring foods still include many mast items which are durable and retain their palatability even into the warmer months. Acorns are a good example of this. Great quantities of new green vegetation are eaten during this period, and insects begin to form a noticeable part of the diet. At this season, the birds may fly into the trees and pick the newly burst buds, tender leaves, and flowers. They will walk precariously about on very small limbs, balancing themselves with outstretched wings. As summer approaches, insects form an ever-increasing portion of the food, especially as the grasshoppers begin to attain good size and abundance. Soft, fleshy fruits are eaten in quantity, as they ripen in summer and early fall.

Fall foods include vast quantities of insects, much seed of grasses, sedges, weeds, and grains, and other late-ripening fruits and berries. Usually, the important winter mast foods are not bothered too much until after several heavy frosts and the early fall foods become scarce.

At any season, the wild turkey is exceedingly adaptable. It can survive deep snows and serious droughts by adjusting to new foods and by taking advantage of every possible opportunity to feed. The deep snows and severe temperatures of winter in Pennsylvania and other northern states provide a real test of their adaptability. The Pennsylvania Game Commission attempts to provide emergency food in the form of yellow corn on the cob during periods of deep snow, but not all birds can be reached. Those without this artificial supplement will eat buds in some quantity much like a ruffed grouse. They will follow the open spring ditches and runs and scratch in the gravel and mud for green vegetation, roots, aquatic insects, crayfish, salamanders, and any other items which might help keep body and soul together.

One of the most striking demonstrations of their adaptability is a close working relationship with the white-tailed deer in this area. Although a turkey can scratch through three or four inches of soft or light snow to the leaf litter below, it has difficulty with anything much deeper than that. Deer, on the other hand, can paw down through a foot or more of snow and stir up the forest floor. The turkeys have discovered this fact and feed extensively in areas which have been pawed over by deer. And they have been observed repeatedly feeding right with the deer. A turkey will stand expectantly by while a deer busily paws a good-sized hold in the snow, and, just as soon as the deer steps back to see what he might have uncovered, the turkey jumps into the hole and begins picking furiously at any food items. The deer seem to tolerate these star boarders quite well and rarely show any real animosity. However, the smaller deer seem to be somewhat shy of these larger birds, and may go through some interesting antics in an attempt to chase the intruders away.

Turkeys have other interesting feeding habits. Except when a hen is saddled with a brood of young poults, turkeys keep on the move almost constantly when feeding. Their progress may be leisurely if food is abundant, or fairly rapid when it is widely scattered. At any rate the daily feeding activities may take them several miles from the daylight starting point. When feeding on mast covered with leaves, the birds will scratch vigorously and may eventually dig up several acres. The whole area may look like it had been rooted over by pigs. When scratching, the birds almost invariably follow a set procedure. They will take a short step forward, extend the left foot about six inches directly in front, and scratch backward and outward in a sweeping, vigorous stroke of about 18 inches. The right foot executes two similar, consecutive motions, and is then followed by a final scratch with the left foot. This is all done quickly and vigorously and is invariably followed by raising the head and surveying the surroundings for a moment to be sure that no danger threatens. The inverted V formed by this operation is about eighteen inches long.

A flock may spend several hours on a few acres when acorns or some other preferred food is scattered abundantly in the leaves. When a large flock is busily scratching, the rustling of the leaves can be heard for two or three hundred yards on a quiet day. When moving from one feeding area to another, the birds will pick at any food item which may attract their attention. Thus, a single turkey crop has been found to contain as many as 61 different items. This hen killed in Virginia in May, 1939, had consumed the following items: 12 whole acorns and pieces of others from 5 different kinds of oaks; several blades of an unidentified grass; several blades of panic grass; 131 seed heads, loose seeds, and leaves of sedge; several leaves of solomon's seal; 2 seeds of greenbrier; 67 seeds of buttercup; leaves and flowers of a second kind of buttercup; 125 seeds of tall meadow rue; 10 seeds of another species of meadow rue; 11 seeds of hog peanut; 11 seeds of violet; several leaves of blueberry; fragments of plants of hawkweed; 45 flower heads of climbing boneset; 11 flowerheads of rattlesnake root; 588 fruit galls of two species of unidentified insects; 8 or more cockroaches; a stink bug; 4 assassin bugs; 2 adult and larva of ground beetles; 1 adult weevil; 3 click beetles; 3 or more fireflies; 26 beetles of at least 9 species; 1 crane fly; a wasp; 16 ants; 3 spiders; 1 daddy-long-legs; 5 or more millipedes; 3 centipedes; and at least 110 snails of five species.

Some crops collected have contained over one pound of food or about four-fifths of a pint. A bird was killed with 221 red oak acorns in its crop; another had 432 beechnuts and another 419. Still another had eaten 640 flowering dogwood berries and this was only 90 per cent of the crop contents. Smaller seeds are eaten in tremendous numbers.

One bird ate 11,500 seeds of the nimble-will and this was only 18 per cent of its meal. A second had eaten 6,800 seeds of crab grass and this constituted only 5 per cent of the total food.

In 537 stomachs examined in Virginia, 354 species of plants and 313 species of animals were represented. This illustrates the diversity of the wild turkey diet and the bird's remarkable ability to obtain sustenance from so many different sources.

As a flock feeds along, the individuals may be scattered over quite an area depending somewhat upon the total number of birds. A large flock may occupy a quarter acre or more at one time. A turkey which falls a little behind will quicken its pace until it rejoins the group. The rate of travel of a feeding flock is usually about one to two miles an hour or about the speed equivalent to a man walking very slowly. A feeding flock is difficult to approach because one or more of the members is always scanning the surroundings. There appears to be no posted "sentry," but instead each turkey takes a good look every few seconds. For this reason, it is almost impossible to sneak up on a flock unless the hunter can keep completely hidden.

Turkeys exhibit a variety of interesting little antics when feeding. They frequently lift and cross their wings over their backs, and occasionally they jump and run with outstretched wings as if at play. In feeding through grass fields in summer and early fall, the birds may chase grasshoppers and be running wildly in every direction at once. When taking ripe seed from heads of grasses and sedges, they will grasp the stem crosswise in their bills below the seeds and strip upward with a twist of the head. In this manner they can fill their crops in a very short time.

Like most upland game birds, turkeys appear to have two major feeding periods each day. The first is early in the morning shortly after they leave the roost, and the second is in late afternoon not too long before they go to roost. Feeding will continue intermittently throughout the day, except that there are likely to be fairly long periods of midday inactivity in excessively hot weather. During summer rains, the birds are likely to leave the dense forests and feed in open areas. Wild turkeys will regularly stay on their roosting trees for several days during especially severe winter weather without once coming down to attempt to feed. They will not usually move until the storm clears or the weather breaks.

Extensive food habit studies of the wild turkey have not been made for many states. Virginia, Pennsylvania, Missouri, Alabama, Florida, West Virginia, and Maryland are a few states which have had sizeable collections of stomachs or droppings analyzed. Some work has also been done on food habits determination by direct observation of the items eaten.

On all studies made, vegetable foods were found to outweigh greatly the animal foods in importance. Virginia turkeys ate 95% vegetable items and 5% animal material. In West Virginia and Florida, 98% and 97% of the diet was vegetable in nature. A year-round sample in Missouri revealed a 75% vegetable diet and 25% animal matter. Spring food habits studies in Alabama showed that 90% of the volume was vegetable matter, but the winter foods were only 82% vegetable.

The most important class of vegetable foods in states from Missouri east are fruits and seeds. Those which compose the bulk of the wild turkey's diet are acorns, beechnuts, grass seeds, grapes, flowering dogwood, greenbrier, black gum, hackberry, wild cherry, huckleberries, blueberries, dewberries, persimmons, and corn. Naturally many others are taken but on a greatly reduced scale.

In Texas, acorns were still the number one food item. Summer foods there were insects, domestic grains, the seeds of various grasses such as the panics, gramas, dropseeds, paspalums, various fruits like dewberries, blackberries, and grapes, and weed seeds, particularly of goat weed or croton. Winter foods in Texas included acorns, cedar berries, prickly pear, apples, tassajillo fruits, grass seeds, and others.

Florida food studies showed that live oak acorns were the most important single food item in the fall and winter diet. One full crop contained 137 live oak acorns. The eleven top foods from an annual sample were grass leaves, panic grass seed, acorn fragments, *Paspalum*—bullgrass seed, corn, wax myrtle berries, gallberry seed, beetles, carpetgrass seed, grasshoppers and cabbage palm berries.

Seasonal variations in the kinds and amounts of food eaten were also evident in Florida. Grass leaves and seeds were used extensively in spring and summer, but pine and acorn mast, gallberry, and wax myrtle consumption diminished. Cabbage palm berries and cypress seed were eaten in small amounts throughout the year.

In almost all states, the acorn was considered the number one mast food and was designated the "staff of life" for wild turkeys by one biologist. When available, these nuts are eaten at all seasons of the year in quantity except during the summer months when they are usually all consumed or have sprouted and disintegrated. All kinds of acorns are eaten by turkeys and are usually swallowed whole with the possible exception of the large-fruited kinds such as the bur oak, the overcup oak, and the swamp chestnut oak. Pieces of these are taken after they have been broken by squirrels, hogs, or other animals. Missouri wild turkey biologists found that the post and blackjack oaks were most attractive out of seven species used regularly.

Beechnuts are another nut food and appear to be one of the favorites. They will regularly eat beechnuts in preference to acorns, but seldom do turkeys have this choice over much of the range. The beech crop is extremely irregular in most places, and nuts in quantity are seldom produced any oftener than every four to five years on the average. This brings up the point that the examination of the crop contents of game birds does not necessarily indicate their favorite foods or those most palatable to them. Like humans, who will eat hamburger if they do not have T-bone steak, wild birds must substitute availability for desirability. Nevertheless, if the bitter or tasteless foods keep the birds well nourished and healthy, it makes little difference in the long run whether they like them or not. Actually, upland game birds probably do not have a highly developed sense of taste anyway, and they probably have few pronounced likes and dislikes.

Flowering dogwood and other dogwoods are valuable food plants for this bird. The red fruits and seeds of the flowering dogwood are available through much of the year, and constitute a good part of the diet wherever it occurs. Fruiting of this species is quite dependable as well, so that it maintains its rank as one of the most valuable food sources year after year. The other dogwood fruits are eaten in quantity but most of these are available for only a short time after ripening.

Black gum is used extensively in the more southern areas of eastern United States, but the fruit is not so palatable nor available for so long a period as the flowering dogwood.

Various viburnums are excellent wild turkey foods, but again most of the fruits are gone shortly after ripening. Many of these small berries and fruits are eaten by small non-game birds and the bushes may be cleaned in a very few days. Probably two of the best viburnums are the black haw and the sweet viburnum commonly called "wild raisins." Both of these shrubs produce sweet, prune-like fruits, commonly eaten by hunters and old favorites of turkeys and grouse.

The wild grape, where it occurs, ranks very high as a wild turkey food, and from a management standpoint is one of the most desirable. The wild grape is eaten by almost any game bird and mammal and many furbearers as well. Deer, bears, grouse, squirrels, foxes, opossums, and many others besides the turkey relish the flavor of this fruit. The grape has a characteristic which makes it an especially desirable winter food. Many times a portion of the crop will remain attached to the vines even into late winter and a few pods or loose grapes may be found scattered on the snow when food is scarcest. The birds can also fly into the vines and pick the dried fruit during periods of emergency when the ground is covered with deep snow.

In the northern hardwoods forests of northern Pennsylvania and on some of the tops of the higher Appalachians farther south, the oak is a rare tree. The bulk of the timber is composed of birch, beech, maple, and black cherry. Because the birches and maples produce little mast food and the beechnut is so irregular in fruiting, the wild cherry is the staple forest-tree food of the wild turkey. These dried fruits and seeds persist throughout the winter and into the spring. However, deep snows in these areas often make such foods unavailable, and the wild turkey must subsist for a time on items it can obtain above the snow or in open springs or streams. It is not uncommon in these northern forests to have an almost complete mast crop failure during some years. Then the turkey must demonstrate its versatility and adaptability to survive. Then the seeds of witch hazel, American hornbeam, maple, ash, and other miscellaneous trees and shrubs are eaten until the supply is exhausted. Green forage, roots, and bulbs become more important if the birds can get to the forest floor. And the spring runs are worked hard for animal and vegetable items. In the north, this is the time that the turkey appreciates ear corn in feeders serviced by game wardens or thoughtful sportsmen.

Another fall and winter food which deserves mention is the greenbrier. This Smilax produces a dark blue to black berry which hangs on the vine until mid-winter. The fruits are eaten readily by turkeys and grouse, and the leaves which remain green the year around are also eaten by both birds as forage. Greenbrier should be encouraged in wild turkey management. The hackberry produces a dry, hard fruit which is also eaten during winter.

Summer and fall foods for adult turkeys almost always occur in superabundance, so that in management they are

much less important than winter foods over the more northern parts of the wild turkey range. Aside from insects, the
more important sources of nutrition are various fleshy fruits
and berries such as huckleberries, blueberries, dewberries,
blackberries, raspberries, persimmons, and a host of others.
Perhaps more important than these are the seeds of various
grasses and sedges. These tiny seeds are produced by the tons
and are stripped as they mature. Considering both the green
forage and the seeds furnished by these plants, they are
exceedingly valuable during this period of the year, especially to the growing poults.

Insects furnish much-needed protein for growing poults
and for egg-laying hens. Without this supplement to the
vegetable diet, it is doubtful whether poult rearing could
be successful in most places. Grasshoppers and beetles of
many kinds form the bulk of the animal life eaten, but the
ants and termites are also taken in quantity. Besides insects,
crayfish, snails, slugs, centipedes, millipedes, salamanders and
other miscellaneous animal life are eaten with some regularity. In management, insects can be encouraged by creating
grassy openings in forests and by planting edges or openings
with various grasses and legumes known to support large
numbers of grasshoppers. Power line rights-of-way across
wooded areas are ideal for this purpose.

*Chapter 5:*

# Natural Enemies and Other Limiting Factors

## *Before Hatching*

LIKE all game birds, turkeys experience high nesting losses. In Virginia, only one-third of 27 wild turkey nests under observation were successful. In Missouri, 11 (37.9%) of 29 nests hatched. Only 28.6 per cent of 14 nests in Pennsylvania and 11.1 per cent of 9 nests in Arizona produced poults. An early study in Alabama showed 80 per cent success in nests located, but a later study indicated only a 50 per cent survival. Considering all nests collectively, the success rate was about 41 per cent for ground nesting birds in general.

Causes of nesting failure are many. Probably the most important single reason for failure is nest desertion. This is principally caused by man and his dogs. Man is also to blame in some cases for illegally stealing the eggs and attempting to raise the wild birds. Almost without exception, this venture is doomed to fail, because the average individual does not have sufficient knowledge to rear the poults successfully. If they use a chicken for a foster mother, the poults are almost sure to contract blackhead from her and die anyway. During the early stages of incubation, a truly wild hen will desert readily, perhaps even from having been flushed from her nest just once by a man, dog, or other animal.

The second most important cause of nest losses is predation. Egg destruction by birds and mammals is a common occurrence for almost any ground-nesting bird. Over the country, the list of worst egg predators would vary considerably. In the Northeast, the raccoon, crow, mink, fox, skunk, opossum, dog, rattlesnake, and blacksnake would head the list. Red squirrels and chipmunks may also be held accountable for egg stealing at times. In the South most of these same egg predators are active, and the domestic hog and the cotton rat probably should be added. Also, the king snakes, pine snakes, chicken snakes and cottonmouth moccasin could be included as possibilities. Farther west the coyote, civet cat, ringtail, and prairie racer will destroy nests and eggs regularly, as well as foxes, raccoons, and crows. Armadillos and road runners are evidently not important nest predators.

It is hardly necessary to say that any predator which kills the incubating hen while on the nest or when off feeding or drinking has effectively finished one more clutch of eggs since the gobbler never takes part in incubation as the male bobwhite does.

Some egg predators leave telltale signs at the nest which serve to identify the culprit. Crows will peck holes in the middle of the egg and drink the contents. The skunk will usually bite off the small end and lap the liquid egg from the ground. Dogs crush the eggs and may separate the contents from the shell inside the mouth and drop the crushed shell to the ground. Opossums may carry an egg away before eating it, and according to one observation an egg the size of a turkey's may be carried in the curled tail. (I have actually seen an opossum carrying leaves for its nest in this manner). Foxes, too, may carry the eggs for some distance before crushing them. The raccoon picks up the egg in its "hands" and bites them open. Snakes always swallow them whole and usually unbroken. The common box turtle is often accused of eating wild turkey eggs, but experiments by the writer proved that they are incapable of breaking eggs which they cannot get inside their mouths. Thus, their destruction is confined to eggs not much larger than those of the bobwhite quail. Woodchucks, gray squirrels, and a host of other mammals have been accused of nest robbery. Ravens and magpies are two more suspects.

Beside desertion and predation, there are several other causes of nesting failures. A wild turkey study in Pennsylvania disclosed that a fairly important loss occurred from mowing. Hens occasionally place their nests in hay meadows and were crippled or frightened by the mower to the extent that they would desert, even though the farmer might leave an "island" of grass around the nest. However, it was found that the great majority of these cultivated-field nesters were game farm birds which were released not long before the nesting season began. Few truly wild hens will nest in such vulnerable spots.

Another cause of nesting failure characteristic of the newly released game farm hen is that of the hen dying during incubation. In spite of all known medications and precautions to date, many of the wild turkeys released from state game farms are carrying blackhead (enterohepatitis). After release and the cessation of medication, these birds may die of the disease about the time egg laying has been completed and incubation started. These birds have been found dead on or near the nest.

Forest fires and grass fires can easily be the cause of many lost nests and even of adult losses if they occur during the height of the nesting season. Needless to say, cooked eggs are hardly likely to hatch.

On the opposite extreme, torrential rains and floods may destroy nests or cause them to be deserted. Flooding is rarely as important as fire as a destructive force, however, because most nests are on higher, well drained ground and often on the spongy forest litter which is capable of absorbing immense quantities of water.

Other minor factors are infertility, freezing, and breakage when the hen is suddenly frightened from the nest. Usually fertility is zero or one hundred per cent. In the wild there are few cases of sterility in gobblers, but a few have been recorded. At least two gobblers, during the years the Pennsylvania Game Commission maintained breeding pens in the mountains, were found to be sterile or impotent. This may be associated with injury of some kind, perhaps from gunshot wounds. In the more northern states, sub-freezing weather before incubation starts may freeze or chill the eggs to the extent that the germ is killed. This is not common, but occurs every few years, especially in some of the frost pocket areas. When a hen is suddenly frightened and she flies from her nest, she may break one or more eggs. This may happen if a predator springs at the hen or a human walks too close.

It should be remembered in this connection that even though a first clutch of eggs is destroyed, it does not necessarily mean that the hen will not nest successfully on another attempt. If a nest is destroyed prior to hatching, the hen is likely to lay a second clutch and try again. In fact, under favorable circumstances she may even try a third time. This characteristic is extremely desirable for the survival and prosperity of any game bird. If turkeys were single-nested and all hens nested at about the same time, any major catastrophe such as might be caused by weather, fire, excessive predator pressure, or other force might come close to wiping out the birds in that locality. This is Nature's way of compensating for the inevitable high losses in nests.

### Poult Losses

Mortality in young turkey poults begins where egg predation and nest destruction ends. Many of the same forces which caused trouble during the egg laying and incubation stages continue to cut into the potential hunting season population of wild turkeys. The more active predators such as foxes, coyotes, dogs, and others which ate eggs will continue to catch and destroy poults at every opportunity. Fire and floods continue to take their toll by destroying many broods of poults while they are still relatively flightless.

But there are now many new and different dangers to be faced. Many new predators are added to the old list. During the first few weeks, the tiny poults are vulnerable to even the smaller hawks and owls. Cooper's and sharp-shinned hawks may take their toll in spite of the watchful eye of the mother. Weasels, house cats, and other small mammals attack from the ground. In Texas, rock squirrels killed and ate two turkey poults about one week old, and probably the red squirrel in the East will do the same. Even adult gobblers have been known to kill young poults by picking them on top of the head, but this is believed to be a comparatively rare occurrence since the hen tends to shy away from any gobblers she may meet.

Accidents are a prime cause of mortality during the early

ages. Young poults which fall into holes, ditches, or other depressions in the ground or rocks, are eventually left by the hen when they do not respond to her calls. One writer tells of hens flying across a creek or some other body of water and then calling her chicks. When they attempt to swim across several may drown before she seems to realize her mistake and flies back.

One of the greatest single causes of juvenile mortality is inclement weather. Young wild turkey poults are especially susceptible to wetting and chilling, and they are not too resistant even at six weeks of age. One brief summer thundershower, if the poults are not protected under the wings of the hen, is sufficient to kill any strayed individuals. Or if the shower should occur just after the hen was frightened from her charges by humans or some predator, she may lose her entire brood.

The worst situation of all is a cold three to five day rain shortly after the peak of hatching. Even the most attentive hen may keep her babies under her wings and in the dry for twenty-four or thirty-six hours, but eventually she must move in a desperate attempt to find food for them. As they pick up water in their down feathers from the rain drops or from the wet grass or brush, they quickly chill. As one becomes too weak and listless to attempt to keep up with the remainder of the family, it stands with wings and head drooping and cries pitifully. Within a few minutes it will be prostrate, and, unless rescued by human hands, it has joined the ranks of perhaps hundreds of others which were the victims of the same "wet spell." Thus, an untimely cold rain in late spring can mean the difference between good hunting and poor hunting during the following open season.

When a hen loses a brood, she does not renest as she does when she merely loses a nest of eggs.

Disease is another cause of poult mortality. On game farms, young wild turkeys are susceptible to many of the diseases experienced by domestic turkey breeders. Coccidiosis if not controlled by medication can be one of the worst, but its degree of prevalence in the wild is not known. Probably some loss may be attributed to this disease. Studies in Pennsylvania produced good evidence that hens released in late winter or early spring could impart blackhead to their susceptible poults later in the year. Evidently some adult turkeys may recover from a light case of blackhead or possess a partial natural immunity to the disease and remain "carriers" perhaps for the rest of their lives. At about five to eight weeks of age, the poults seem to be most susceptible and the protozoa causing blackhead are transmitted to the young birds via the droppings of the hen. Sooner or later a part of the youngsters will be infected when they eat food contaminated by the hen. Many broods were found to be lost, either wholly or in part, in this manner. Even in truly wild broods there is a chance for blackhead infection from poultry manure scattered on fields.

These are the major causes of juvenile losses, but there are undoubtedly others of lesser significance or even some yet undiscovered.

Instances have been uncovered wherein a parent hen has been killed when her brood was only a few weeks old and most of the youngsters survived and grew normally. In one such case in West Virginia, the birds were only a little larger than bobwhite quail when the hen was destroyed by a predator. Eight of her brood were still present in October, but, like most wild babies which grow up without parental guidance, they possessed little fear of men. An unusually hot, dry spring and early summer probably explains any brood survival of this kind.

### Adult Predation

Throughout most of the range of the wild turkey in North America, predation upon adult birds is not sufficiently severe to be considered a primary reduction factor. Naturally, many older turkeys are killed by the larger and more potent predators, but this loss is relatively insignificant compared to the nesting and juvenile mortality already described.

Few raptorial birds or carnivirous mammals are large enough or active enough to catch and kill many adult wild turkeys. Among the birds, the great horned owl, the golden eagle, and the bald eagle appear to be the main offenders. Foxes, bobcats, coyotes, wolves, and dogs are the outstanding mammalian predators, with the raccoon as another possibility.

The great horned owl was found to be the worst offender in Pennsylvania on the game farm hens being held in open pens in the mountains. These birds which were being held there to breed with wild gobblers to improve the quality of the game farm stock were taken frequently by horned owls and had to be protected by pole traps and other owl control measures. Raccoons were also destructive in these enclosures, but it should be remembered that these birds were artificially reared and were also wing-clipped to prevent them from leaving the area. An attendant at one of these propagation areas also saw an adult red-tailed hawk attack a fully grown hen and knock her from a limb, but it did not have an opportunity to complete the kill because it was quickly dispatched with a shotgun.

At various game farms in the East, the horned owl is often a prime nuisance. They attack at night and may kill several birds at one visit. They also create a nervousness among the surviors which tends to cause the birds to leave the pens and fly into the surrounding woods. For these reasons, losses can be severe. Because the owls do not always return to a kill, they are also difficult to control.

In the wild also, horned owls are a menace to adult turkeys. There appears to be some disagreement as to how a horned owl makes its kill. Audubon tells how they often escape from being killed: "As turkeys usually roost in flocks, on naked branches of trees, they are easily discovered by their enemies, the owls, which, on silent wing, approach and hover around them for the purpose of reconnoitering. This, however, is rarely done without being discovered, and a single cluck from one of the turkeys announces to the whole party the approach of the murderer. They instantly start upon their legs, and watch the motions of the owl, which selecting one as its victim, comes down upon it like an arrow, and would inevitably secure the turkey, did not the latter at that moment lower its head, stoop, and spread its tail in an inverted manner over its back, by which action the aggressor is met by a smooth inclined plane, along which it glances without hurting the turkey; immediately after which the latter drops to the ground, and thus escapes, merely with the loss of a few feathers."

McIlhenny, on the other hand, describes actual observations made by an acquaintance. He claims that the owl lights on the same limb with the turkey between it and the tree.

The owl then moves along the limb toward the turkey and when almost to it voices a low "whoo, whoo." The victim utters the alarm note and moves toward the end of the limb. After repeating this performance a few times, the turkey reaches the end of the limb and is forced to fly and is promptly caught in the air. Concensus of opinion seems to be that this is the more common pattern of attack, but in all probability Audubon's description is also correct at times.

In spite of the fact that the horned owl is one of the worst predators of adult turkeys in the East, the total losses from all causes in an ordinary winter are not great. Overwintering losses in adult turkeys was found to be less than five per cent on a study-area in Pennsylvania.

Both eagles are reputed to catch and kill wild turkeys but little information concerning the extent of damage is available. Golden eagles have been observed in the act of killing introduced wild turkeys in California. A biologist in South Dakota reports that the introduced Merriam's turkey appears to fear the bald and golden eagles more than any other natural enemy. He states: "Eighty to ninety birds have been observed feeding several hundred yards from cover when, it seemed, for no apparent reason, one of the old guards would give the danger signal and the whole flock would burst into the air and fly to the nearest cover. On looking up into the air an eagle would be seen flying near the area."

Probably the eagles, like the horned owl, take relatively few wild turkeys and may have little effect upon the total population in the long run. Certainly until they are proven to be a serious limiting factor, these magnificent birds should not be killed indiscriminately.

Collectively, the foxes may be the worst single mammalian predator on adult wild turkeys. The red and gray foxes are found distributed over much of the turkey range in North America, although the gray fox is confined to a much more restricted area. Even these capable predators are not considered to be a serious controlling factor once the wild turkey is well established. However, when artificially reared birds are being introduced to a new area, losses to foxes and other carnivorous animals sometimes can mean the difference between success and failure.

Fred A. Glover analyzed 473 fox scats (droppings) as a part of his *Wild Turkey Investigation in West Virginia*. These scats were all collected on the wild turkey range of that state. Wild turkey remains were found in nine of these samples, all collected between January and March, 1947. This was a severe winter, and many turkeys were in a weakened condition because of the deep snows and subsequent lack of food. There is also reason to believe that several of the nine occurrences may have resulted from a single kill, because a full stomach of turkey will produce as many as three or four different droppings, and at this time of the year a fox may return to the carcass to feed over a period of several days until it is entirely consumed.

Several hundred stomachs of both red and gray foxes examined by the writer and several thousand fox scats analyzed by E. L. Kozicky and the writer from the wild turkey range of Pennsylvania contained no identifiable remains of this bird. However, as always, there were some unidentified birds which could conceivably have been wild turkeys. Particularly in scats, the only remaining portion of a bird may be the quill tops of feathers. Except for size, these have little meaning. Also, it is almost impossible to differentiate between domestic and wild turkeys in scats and even in stomachs. For these reasons, studies of this kind do not give positive figures.

Of greater value are actual observations of kills or of escapes. Such incidents may be witnessed by wildlife workers or by anyone spending time in the outdoors. In the more northern states, the story is often written very plainly in the snow. Game Protectors in Pennsylvania have often reported seeing where a fox has followed turkeys but almost invariably was unsuccessful in killing one. The fox is known to follow at times until it is sure of the direction of travel and then attempt to cut off the birds by circling in front of them. This strategy appears to be doomed to failure most of the time as well.

A hunter in McKean County, Pennsylvania on the first morning of the deer season took his favorite stand just before daylight. After a short time he discovered a flock of turkeys roosting in the trees nearby. A little later one flew down to the ground. It made a funny noise and flew right back up. Several more did the same thing. The hunter suspected something was wrong and investigated. He got close enough to see that every time a turkey hit the ground a red fox would make a dive for it. The fox discovered the hunter before he could get a shot at it and disappeared into the brush.

The healthy, native wild turkey is seldom outwitted by a fox, because its exceedingly keen eyesight and ability to escape quickly by flying are good insurance against an animal which attacks in this manner. Even the crippled turkey is not always vulnerable. One of the biologists working for the Pennsylvania Game Commission can attest to this fact. Although part of the breast was blown away by a .22 Hornet bullet from his gun, a turkey fought off repeated attacks from a fox (probably a red) during the night and was still very much alive when he arrived on the scene again the next morning. This incident will be described in greater detail in a later chapter entitled *Choosing the Proper Rifle, Ammunition, and Sights.*

Mosby and Handley were able to account for 276 out of 440 pen-reared wild turkeys stocked in the fall of 1940 to July, 1941. Of this number, 43 were known to have been killed by predators, and 34 of the 43 were taken by foxes. Bobcats killed three others, and the remaining six were lost to unknown predators.

Mosby tells of reconstructing the details of one attack upon an adult gobbler by a gray fox from the tracks. The gobbler was feeding in a small opening, and the fox was able to approach within 20 feet behind a screen of thick vegetation. When the bird's back was turned, the fox dashed toward it and grabbed it by the neck. A real struggle ensued but the turkey was finally killed and partially eaten. Evidence, however, would indicate that these tactics are not often successful.

Individually, the bobcat is believed by many to be a more competent turkey killer than the foxes. This is probably true, but it is badly outnumbered by the foxes and coyote over much of the turkey range. But, as in the case of the foxes and other predators, adult losses to the wildcat are not believed to be severe in well-established wild populations. Both McIlhenny and Davis tell about many occasions when bobcats have been called up to a hunter using the turkey call. In one case at least, the hunter was attacked as he lay behind a log, although it is probable that he was mistaken for a turkey. In at least two other instances, the cats appeared to be rather indifferent or nonchalant about their stalking, and were believed to be more curious than bloodthirsty. McIlhenny was of the opinion that turkeys are not particularly afraid of wildcats, and will stand their ground quite well unless the animal gets too near or dashes toward them. Audubon claimed that the bobcat would lie in wait for a feeding flock and spring upon a victim from a convenient perch such as a rock or limb.

The coyote in the middlewestern and western states is likely an even more capable adult turkey predator than the fox principally because of his size. But again, it probably kills a very small percentage of the total number.

Bob Gage in reporting on the wild turkeys in the Black Hills of South Dakota tells of an incident wherein a coyote had treed about 50 birds in a scrub oak thicket. But on the ground an immense gobbler had elected to stay and fight, and fight he did. The coyote appeared to be getting the worst of the deal when the human intruder frightened off the whole lot.

A similar instance of a gobbler attacking an animal much larger than itself was told by a fox hunter from McKean County, Pennsylvania where men are men and turkeys are afraid of nothing apparently. One morning as the men and hounds were slowly working a piece of timber in the hope of picking up a fresh fox track, one of the large hounds ran into a flock of turkeys. He was attacked almost immediately by the protector of the flock. This big bird literally rode on the back of the terror-stricken dog, flogging him unmercifully with its wings and feet. With a great amount of yelping and ki-yi-ing, the big hound ran to the feet of its master and would not leave again until they were quite some distance from the scene. The same performance was repeated not more than a week later, and this fox hunter now has a turkey-shy hound!

There is every reason to believe that foxes and other smaller predators receive the same treatment on many occasion. It is obvious from tracks in the snow that foxes have followed turkeys and never could muster the courage to attack these big birds. Many more escape, even after the animal has a secure grip with his teeth, by beating and scratching the animal with wings and feet. Anyone who has handled many turkeys knows how severe this treatment can be.

One of the most obvious proofs that predation is not a serious controlling factor in most areas is provided by the recent history of the wild turkey in Pennsylvania. In a little over ten years the range was expanded from two million acres to thirteen million acres, and the annual hunting season harvest increased from about four thousand to sixteen thousand turkeys. This occurred during a period when foxes, opossums and raccoons were at an all-time high for the State, and horned owls, hawks, crows, stray dogs and cats, and countless smaller predators were at least at normal levels.

## Legal Hunting and Poaching

Many species of wildlife are definitely underharvested. The white-tailed deer is a prime example of this, particularly in those states with a "buck law." In other game species, the hunting season kill is only a small part of the total mortality (usually under twenty per cent) and much more liberal seasons and bag limits could be permitted without endangering the future supply of these animals. Rabbits, squirrels, ruffed grouse, and, in many places, quail fall into this category. But on the other hand, hunting can have a decided influence on future stocks of other game species. In regions easily accessible to large numbers of hunters, the ring-necked pheasant and the wild turkey can be so reduced in numbers that full recovery in one year's time is impossible under average conditions. Of course, where only cock ringnecks are shot, it matters little whether 70% of the males are killed, because it still leaves a number adequate for successful reproduction. The male ringneck is polygamous and will regularly mate with up to a dozen or more hens in a single season.

Except in those states where hunting is restricted to gobbler shooting in the spring, the harvest is normally of both sexes for wild turkeys. Because of the popularity of the sport and the easy access to most good turkey country via improved roads, many flocks may be exposed to intense hunting pressure during the long open seasons provided in most states. The importance of accessibility of range is demonstrated clearly in Pennsylvania. The turkey range in the south-central part of the State is confined largely to the long, parallel mountains and ridges of the Appalachian chain. These steep-sided, narrow-topped mountains are rarely more than a few miles wide and are regularly separated by wide, agricultural valleys. Thus, it is almost impossible for a flock of turkeys to get more than two or three miles from a drivable road in this region. Also, this section of the state is nearest the large centers of population and receives added hunting pressure for this reason. As a result, the hunting season harvest may approach or even exceed 50% of the fall population in these counties.

In contrast, the northern portion of the State is covered by the Allegheny Mountains which are irregularly dissected by many hundreds of streams and rivers flowing in all directions. Much of this area is not conducive to agriculture because the valleys are extremely narrow and the climate relatively severe. As a consequence, much of this region is wooded and unoccupied, and few roads traverse the mountains. It is not uncommon to find comparative "wilderness areas" many thousands of acres in extent without any public roads of entry. Because much of this region is 100 to 200 miles or more from the large population centers, the hunter is often pressed for time, or lacks the necessary strength or energy to penetrate these wilderness areas any great distance. For this reason, some isolated flocks of turkeys may be almost unmolested during the entire season. The kill in many of these counties may not exceed 10 to 20% of the fall population.

In Virginia, the state-wide kill during the season was found to be about 30% of the total number. A detailed study of 28 flocks in scattered counties of that state revealed the loss during the hunting season to be in excess of 52%, with a range from 11% to 100%. The fact that some flocks can be completely wiped out is significant in management, because it may mean that temporary vacuums could exist in many places throughout the range. These empty spots may be refilled by spring stocking of game farm birds, but this is at best an expensive proposition even if successful. Refuges or a more careful control of the harvest might permit these areas to be permanently self-sufficient.

Florida biologists also estimate the annual hunting season kill at about 30% of the total population. To arrive at an average this high, it obviously means that the kill in some areas or of some flocks was far beyond this figure. West Virginia reports a low 12% harvest which is perhaps explainable on the basis of a fairly low human population and a large amount of rugged and isolated mountain country.

Illegal hunting or poaching can sometimes be exceedingly important in keeping a remnant population of wild turkeys in a precarious state, even though the season is closed. Blakey speaking of the illegal kill in the Missouri Ozarks has this to say: "The season of winter snows, the gobbling season of spring, the brooding season of midsummer, the deer season of fall, and any fortuitous opportunity during the daily wanderings of man with gun or club take a far heavier toll of wild turkeys over a large part of the Ozarks than the legal December open season. *The illegal kill by man is the greatest factor limiting the turkey population in Missouri.*

"The midsummer illegal kill, during the first 90 days of the new brood's life, is the worst. On one research area comprising seven townships, whole flocks of turkeys were wiped out and more than 50% of other flocks were killed, all within the 31 days of August, 1936."

Later in 1946, after the wild turkey season had been closed, Dalke, Leopold, and Spencer speaking of the same state added this comment: "We must conclude that in spite of a closed season, hunting losses are still severe, and that the benefits of future improvement in the turkey range cannot be fully realized until the poaching problem is solved."

Hollis found that illegal shooting in Lousiana killed out completely several flocks of young birds in Livingston Parish during the summer of 1946. Flagrant violations were reported from several other parishes.

Throughout the country, illegal shooting continues. The misguided sportsman (?) who has no sense of fair play and the "hill hunter" who believes he has the right to live off the land and to hunt game at any time are actually thieves who are robbing the decent, law-abiding hunter of priceless recreation. These comparatively few individuals are often responsible for the failure of wild turkey introductions into new areas where the bird has been missing for years. And they can prevent the expected increase of struggling flocks even where the bird has existed for a long time. They can mean closed seasons, or short seasons, and may even cause the abandonment of state restoration programs because of their greed and short-sightedness.

Mosby and Handley sum up the situation very well in this terse statement: "The hunter is a very important, probably the most important, single limiting factor on the wild turkey population however disconcerting this fact may be to the sportsmen." The truth of this observation is borne out by past history. Was it not the hunter who took advantage of the plight of the wild turkey when its habitat was partially destroyed by agriculture and lumbering and completed its extirpation over the great bulks of its former range? Until education and common-sense reasoning change the attitude of this minority group of poachers, wild turkey management is going to continue to be an uphill battle in most states.

## Winter Mortality

The term "winter mortality" refers exclusively here to losses resulting from severe climatic conditions, particularly deep snows and severe temperatures. It does not include losses from predation, poaching, disease, or other factors in operation during this period. Naturally, this mortality is restricted to the more northern states on the present fringe of the wild turkey range. However, it is assuming a growing significance as more of these northern states decide to attempt the restoration of the wild turkey. Are these climatic factors an effective barrier to the extension of the wild turkey into forested areas which would otherwise be suitable? Or can this large bird survive severe winter weather if food is available in some form, even if it must be supplied by man during emergency periods?

The wild turkey is an extremely hardy bird, comparing favorably with the ring-necked pheasant in its ability to withstand low temperatures and periods of fasting. Experiments at the wildlife experiment station in Pennsylvania proved this point. Four farm-reared wild turkeys were shut in the climatic chamber there and held without food until they died. Both pairs were subjected to a constant zero temperature, and, in addition, a six mile per hour wind was blown over two of the birds. Another bird was held in an unheated room where the temperature ranged between 34°F. and 50°F. The two birds at zero and in the wind lived seven and nine days, respectively. Those at zero but out of the wind survived eleven and sixteen days. The single bird held in the unheated room lived twenty-four days. Remember, this was without food or water at any time!

As a check, two more were placed in an unprotected outdoor pen in midwinter. These received no food but were able to get some water in the form of snow. Temperatures ranged as low as 9° F. These two birds lived nine and nineteen days. Peculiarly enough the hens of all polygamous game birds seemed to be hardier and could take more cold and starvation than the males. This held true for pheasants and ruffed grouse as well as for the turkeys. In monogamous (pairing) game birds, the male was the stronger. Monogamous species tested were bobwhite quail and Hungarian partridges.

From these experiments, it was concluded that the wild turkey could endure at least one week of severe winter weather without food and suffer no ill effects. It was assumed that the real wild bird would be even more hardy than the game farm stock, because this was found to be true for ring-necked pheasants and bobwhites.

Much other evidence points to the great resistance of the wild turkey. Leon P. Keiser, Superintendent of the Pennsylvania State Wild Turkey Farm, observed an interesting reaction to cold and snow during the very severe 1935-36 winter. About 1000 of his birds were being held in a large field in which a natural stand of Virginia pine formed good roosting cover. During one of the several bad storms of the winter when about 30 inches of snow fell, these birds did not touch food for eight days, although it was placed at the bottom of the trees in which they were roosting. During these days the temperature was below zero most of the time. As soon as the weather moderated a little, the whole flock began to eat voraciously, and the birds appeared to be little the worse for their long fast.

Many times he has had his birds sit for two or three days without once leaving the roost.

This same thing happens in the wild during heavy snow-storms or extremely low temperatures. Repeated observations have been made in Pennsylvania, West Virginia, and Virginia which show that the turkeys will stay in the trees during these periods. Mosby and Handley tell of an incident beginning on January 23, 1940, when 18 to 26 inches of snow fell, and ending February 6 when the snow finally melted to a point where the birds could again move about by walking. The birds moved very little during these two weeks, and, when one did fly down, it would shortly fly back up into the trees again when it found that it could not navigate through the deep, soft snow. During this period, Japanese honeysuckle thickets provided the only natural food known to be taken by the birds. They ate both the green leaves and fruit. In spite of the greatly curtailed movement, reduced food supply, and greater vulnerability to certain types of predation, few, if any, native turkeys were known to be lost during the two weeks.

However, losses do occur under extremely unusual combinations of conditions even when food is available. During the 1935-36 winter, a number of turkeys were known to have died and some of the specimens were examined. Some of these had food in the crop and were in good flesh, so that it was assumed that they died of exposure during the high winds and exceedingly low temperatures (sometimes as low as -35°F.) of that period.

When deep snows cover the food on the ground, turkeys will regularly go to springs and spring runs to scratch for whatever food may be available under water. During this wading and feeding, ice may form on the wet feathers of breast, belly, and tail. This heavy coating of ice will often cause the feathers to pull or break off, leaving the bird without adequate protection against cold. These "bare breasted" birds probably suffer considerably and perhaps die if exposed to long periods of intense cold and high wind. Ice storms in themselves have been blamed for such losses. When freezing rains cover all branches and twigs so that a twig the size of a lead pencil becomes as large around as a hoe handle, the turkey roosting in the open may become so weighted with ice, particularly on its tail feathers, that it is unable to fly or even walk without great difficulty. At the very least, this has a tendency to weaken the bird and make it less resistant to stress. Also, on the ground or on the roost it becomes easy prey to its natural enemies.

In the northern states where severe winter weather can be expected at least occasionally, a program of emergency winter feeding is very desirable and probably necessary. Of course, during many winters, supplemental feeding may not be required, but the mechanics of the program should be set up for quick action when an emergency does arrive. This will be discussed in greater detail under *Winter Feeding*.

## Diseases and Parasites

Certain losses from blackhead have been described under the sections dealing with factors affecting egg production, nesting success, and poult mortality. A brief description will be given of the several diseases and parasites known to be important in the wild.

*Blackhead* or *enterohepatitis* is caused by a microscopic animal called a protozoon. This particular protozoon known

as *Histomonas meleagridis,* appears to be closely associated
with the cecal worm which lives in the caeca, or blindguts,
of the turkeys. An infected bird will become listless, appear droopy, drag its wings, and even stagger in the later
stages. They usually become emaciated, but sometimes
death occurs rather quickly before the bird has lost much
weight. Internal examination will usually reveal a liver
with several large yellow lesions. The two caeca will be
swollen and filled with a cheesy core, and may show evidence of hemorrhaging. Droppings will be liquid and sul-
phur yellow in color.

In its usual form, chickens are immune to the disease and
most small farm flocks seem to be infected with it. Also,
it is an exceedingly prevalent disease on domestic and wild
turkey propagation plants in spite of careful sanitation and
medication to keep it under control. Thus, infection can
be passed to wild stock by direct transfer from released
game farm birds. When wild turkeys feed over the same
ground used by domestic chickens or turkeys, or use fields
fertilized with poultry manure, they are exposed to infection. The protozoa are passed in the droppings of infected
birds, and, when some of this material is picked up on green
vegetation or other contaminated food, the bird is likely
to become diseased. Thus, it is spread from one bird to
another. Free protozoa live only a few hours at most in
these droppings, but when encased in cecal worm eggs, they
may remain infectious for months and perhaps even for
years.

New medications give promise of entirely ridding birds
of these protozoa if treated before release. This could
eliminate one common source of the disease in the wild if

all game farm stock were released free of this organism. Other techniques of blackhead control are being tested as well, including tying off the two caeca so that they cannot serve as reservoirs for the cecal worm and the protozoa. Real progress is expected to be made in the near future on this problem.

Flocks may be subjected to heavy losses from blackhead from early summer to late fall once one bird in the flock becomes infected. When the ground is frozen, the germ is not transmitted from one bird to another very readily, and losses are almost eliminated until the following spring. Even though a bird may recover from blackhead and develop a certain immunity, it evidently remains a "carrier" for the rest of its life. Blackhead has been reported as a serious problem wherever turkeys are found, from Pennsylvania to Florida, from Virginia to Texas and Colorado.

Stoddard made recommendations to prevent undue losses from blackhead in the heavily stocked range of south Georgia. He suggested the yearly rotation of food patches to keep the soil from becoming unnecessarily contaminated; the elimination of free ranging chickens and domestic turkeys; and the discontinuation of the use of poultry manure for field fertilization.

None of the other turkey diseases thus far reported in the wild appear to be anywhere near as important as blackhead as a decimating factor. Coccidiosis (*Eimeria meleagridis*) is a common cause of mortality in poults at the wild turkey game farms in almost any locality. In Pennsylvania, 95 droppings collected in the forests showed a 40% infestation by this organism. It is probable that during some years this disease may cause considerable mortality in the wild, especially during wet springs.

*Leucocytozoon smithi*, a malaria-like blood protozoon, has been found in Virginia and Pennsylvania. In Virginia, 14 of 45 wild birds tested were found positive. In Pennsylvania, blood from 92 farm-reared birds and 5 wild birds was examined, and 20.7% of the game farm birds were infected and all of the wild birds were found to be carrying the disease. This organism is transmitted from one bird to another by the bite of a black fly. The importance of this blood parasite in wild turkeys has not been determined. Wild birds appear to have the power of ridding themselves of it, particulary over winter, and then may become reinfected in the spring. In spite of its prevalence in eastern United States, this may not be a serious cause of mortality.

Among the various other diseases reported in native wild turkeys is a fowl pox (diphtheria) which has caused losses in Florida and perhaps elsewhere. This is a virus disease quite common in chickens. Aspergillosis, caused by the green mold *Aspergillus fumigatus*, has been found in specimens taken in Pennsylvania and Missouri and probably in other states. This fungus affects the lungs, trachae, and air sacs of the birds. Avian monocytosis, commonly called blue comb, has also been identified in wild birds from Pennsylvania.

Apparently few examinations have been made for the common parasites expected to be found in wild turkeys. Whether gapeworm and crop worms which are a common cause of loss in farm-reared birds are also a problem in wild stock has not been determined. It would seem likely that some infestation could occur and probably does, especially during the wet weather of spring and fall when earthworms would be eaten in some quantity. The earthworm is the common intermediate host of both of these parasitic roundworms.

Many more diseases and parasites of wild turkeys have been identified from game-farm stock than from native birds. A list is given below of all those found mentioned in the literature. Undoubtedly others must exist. Perhaps some of the most important have yet to be diagnosed, particularly in wild birds. The diseases are listed according to type and the causative organism is given when known.

## BACTERIAL DISEASES

1. Pullorum or bacillary white diarrhea  *(Salmonella pullorum)*
2. Fowl typhoid  *(Shigella gallinarum)*
3. Fowl cholera  *(Pasteurella avicida)*
4. Avian tuberculosis  *(Mycobacterium avium)*
5. Botulism  *(Clostridium botulinum)*
6. Paratyphoid  *(Salmonella sp.)*
7. Ulcerative enteritis  *(Corynebacterium perdicum)*

## VIRUS DISEASES

Fowl pox *(diphtheria)*

## FUNGUS DISEASES

1. Aspergillosis  *(Aspergillus fumigatus)*
2. Thrush  *(Saccharomyces albicans)*

# INTERNAL PARASITES

## Protozoon Diseases

1. Coccidiosis            (*Eimeria meleagridis* or *Eimeria melegrimitis*)
2. Blackhead or enterohepatitis    (*Histomonas meleagridis*)
3. Trichomoniasis         (*Trichomonas sp.*)
4. Leucocytozoon          (*Leucocytozoon smithi*)
5. Haemoproteus           (*Haemoproteus sp.*)

## INTERNAL WORMS

1. Flukes                 (*Trematoda*)
2. Tapeworm               (*Cestoda*)
3. Gapeworm               (*Syngamus trachea*)
4. Crop worm              (*Capillaria sp.*)
5. Stomach and gizzard worms    (*Nematoda*)
6. Intestinal roundworms  (*Ascaridia galli*)
7. Cecal worm             (*Heterakis gallinae*)

## EXTERNAL PARASITES

1. Lice                   (*Mallophoga*)
2. Mites                  (*Acarina*)
3. Ticks                  (*Acarina*)
4. Hippoboscid flies      (*Diptera*)

In summary, it can be stated that diseases and parasites may be one of the most important factors restricting the numbers of wild turkeys on presently occupied range and retarding the further expansion of the range. And the presence of diseases and parasites in farm-reared birds would suggest a cessation of a program of stocking in the wild, once a newly established population appeared to be self-perpetuating.

## Accidental Deaths

Mortality from accidental causes is not common among adult wild turkeys. A few are killed annually in Pennsylvania and other states on the highways by fast traveling automobiles. Occasionally through misjudgment or because the bird is disturbed in the late evening or after dark, it may fly into telephone or electric wires or even into sharp stubs sticking out of the side of a tree. These birds may die of broken necks or breast wounds. In February, 1955, a Game Protector in Pennsylvania found a hen turkey hanging by its neck about 15 feet from the ground in the narrow fork of a small tree. Evidently, the bird got its neck wedged in the tight fork and its head prevented it from pulling loose.

Two unusual cases of mortality from eating foreign objects were recorded in 1953 in Pennsylvania. A turkey had swallowed an entire .30-06 cartridge case, and this had effectively blocked the movement of food from the gizzard into the small intestine. The bird had literally starved to death with a full stomach. Another had eaten three .22 cartridge cases, but this was not proved to be the sole cause of death, however.

## Competition

The word "competition" as here used may refer to the direct rivalry for food or living space between two or more animals or it may refer to indirect ill-effects brought on by the presence or living habits of other animals. The first is certainly paramount in most areas, but sometimes the second can assume great significance as well. For example, in some sections of the country deer and turkeys occupy the same range. Where deer have not been harvested closely enough and have been permitted to exceed the carrying capacity of the range in terms of the food supply, it is often possible for them to overbrowse the forest growth so severely that a large part of the food-producing shrubs and plants are destroyed. These "deer deserts" will support practically no ruffed grouse, cottontail rabbits, snowshoe hares or other ground-dwelling small game which require low growth for food or security. The wild turkey is much less affected than the others, but even it may "feel the pinch." The loss of this ground cover and shrub layer markedly reduces the amount of green forage, seed, fruits, and insects available to the birds. Fortunately, wild turkeys neither need nor want too much ground growth for protective cover, so that they are more tolerant to this over-browsed condition than other forest small game species. In western states, overbrowsing and overgrazing by elk, mule deer, and cattle produce the same results in many areas that whitetails do in more eastern states.

The direct competition for food is an obvious struggle which goes on throughout the entire year. This sometimes can involve some of the most innocent appearing animals. One of the most common woods dwellers is the white-footed mouse *(Peromyscus)*. This little mouse occurs by the millions over large areas of forest, and each harvests and stores large quantities of seeds and nuts for winter use. The rotten crown of a large beech tree was found to contain at least a peck of good beechnuts stored there by a pair of these mice. The seeds of basswood, wild cherry, flowering dogwood, and many, many others have been found stored in stumps and hollow logs in large quantity. Several quarts of clean clover seed were found in a stump in a clover field in New York, and these seeds were collected by a family of deer mice.

These are only one of many species of small rodents which eat and store food which would otherwise be eaten by game. In fact, the mice and squirrels probably provide the greatest amount of competition to wild turkeys and other forest game birds. The red-backed mouse (*Clethrionomys*) is another which stores great quantities of mast. Chipmunk (*Tamias*) caches have been found which contained a bushel of hazelnuts. These ground squirrels will also store large numbers of hickory nuts, acorns, beechnuts, and other nuts and seeds which are all good wild turkey foods. Fox, gray, and red squirrels eat more tons of these foods annually. In the West, other ground squirrels, gophers, and mice replace the eastern forms in stealing the mast before the game can get it.

Countrywide, probably deer are the next worst offenders. These animals, which eat anywhere from four to twelve pounds of food a day depending upon their size, can be a real competitor to the wild turkey for winter mast. The whitetail is especially fond of acorns, beechnuts, wild grapes, and other nuts and fruits which might otherwise be available to forest game birds. In northern Pennsylvania, where deer have been particularly abundant and mast crops are likely to be light and irregular, the whitetails will devour any mast which falls almost as fast as it hits the ground. Fortunately, the smaller seeds and fruits are relatively untouched by deer, but this does not mean that mice and other rodents permit these foods to lie on the ground for any length of time. As mentioned earlier, however, deer can be a real aid to turkeys during periods of deep snows when they paw down to bare ground and permit these birds to pick up some food in the forest litter.

In the West, the mule deer may be responsible for reducing the total food supply in the several states where the ranges of the two species coincide. Also, range cattle may in some cases be serious rivals of the turkeys for certain preferred foods.

Farther south, particulary in the Southeast, open range hogs become the most important competitor. In these southern states thousands of domestic pigs are permitted to roam at large to find food wherever they can. These animals forage among the oaks, pecans, pines, and other mast trees and consume tremendous quantities of these wild foods.

It is doubtful whether any other species except the various rodents, deer, and domestic livestock compete seriously with the wild turkey for food. As far as it can be determined, in few places would there be a real conflict for space. There appears to be a reasonable tolerance to animal interference or crowding by these large birds, but not to human habitations or activities. Therefore, it would seem that man provides the only noticeable competition for space.

It should be pointed out once more that competition for food, as provided by many animal species, may not be a significant limiting factor. It is believed by the writer that, except under extremely unusual conditions, wild turkeys are capable of securing sufficient food for adequate nutrition so long as they are able to get to the bare ground. Only when snows are deep are they likely to face a real crisis. This is because the bird has the ability to find and utilize such a great variety of vegetable and animal materials for food.

# PART II

## MANAGEMENT OF THE WILD TURKEY IN THE UNITED STATES

*Chapter 6:*

## The Pennsylvania Story

THE recent success in wild turkey management achieved
by the Pennsylvania Game Commission is truly a Cinderella
story. It is going to be told here to illustrate that great numbers of game animals can still exist and can still be restored
to depleted areas in spite of our present civilization and tremendous population growth. It is going to be told to encourage other northern states falling within the former
range of the wild turkey to attempt restoration of this
noblest of game birds. And it is going to be told as a tribute
to scientific game management and to the efforts of those
responsible for this triumph.

For at least 75 years, the wild turkey had not flourished
north of an imaginary line running across central Pennsylvania. This appeared to be the Maginot Line or the Great
Wall as far as the turkey was concerned. Prior to the 1940's,
it was believed that this line coincided fairly closely to the
division between the oak-pine forests to the south and the
birch-beech-maple forests to the north. The thought was
that the northern hardwoods did not produce a dependable
mast crop to hold these large birds over the winter, particularly under the more severe temperatures and deeper snows
encountered in the northern counties of Pennsylvania and
on into New York and New England. A good crop of
beechnuts could not be expected oftener than every five
to seven years on the average, and even the lesser desirable
wild cherry could not be depended upon every year. Maples,
birch, and the various understory trees and shrubs were

all comparatively light producers of game bird food. On the other hand, the oaks to the south were fairly dependable, and the tons of mast produced in the form of acorns provided a top quality winter diet. Grapes, dogwoods, viburnums, and other trees and shrubs supplemented the acorn crop, so that there was seldom a food shortage. Thus, there appeared to be good reasons biologically why the wild turkey would probably remain a southern game bird.

But then, almost explosively, in the early 1940's a few scattered flocks appeared north of this barrier. From this meager beginning, the turkey swept like wildfire across the entire northern part of Pennsylvania and is now spilling across the borders into New York. Peculiarly enough, the northern half of the State now has far more turkeys than the southern half. Fully three-fourths of the estimated 20,000 wild turkeys killed in Pennsylvania during the 1954 season were taken on this new range where there were no turkeys fifteen years ago.

This extension of the range northward is causing quite a stir in the Northeast. New York and the New England states are beginning to dream of the possibility of wild turkey hunting in the near future, and already some of these states are making exploratory surveys and investigations. Perhaps there is even hope for the forested states of the Midwest? And why not, after all the wild turkey once roamed the region as far north as Maine and southern Ontario and west into the Lake States.

The early history of this noble game bird in Pennsylvania and surrounding states illustrates man's greed and disregard for the preservation of his wildlife heritage. Turkeys were hunted as relentlessly as any predator ever has been. Market hunting of wild turkeys flourished as it did for ducks, bob-whites, and wild pigeons. They were taken in every conceivable manner without any thought of the future. They were killed while on the roost and a "good shot" could drop a whole flock, one at a time. The turkey call played havoc with lovesick gobblers in the spring. Even nesting hens were shot and their eggs left to rot. Blinds, pens, set-guns, traps, snares and artificial lights all added to the toll. Dogs were used extensively to "bark them up." It is little wonder that by the beginning of the 20th century the wild turkey was nearly extinct in Pennsylvania. Surely, these were some of the blackest pages in conservation history.

But there were other problems beside this uncontrolled shooting which contributed to the gradual disappearance of the turkey in the northeastern states. Thousands and thousands of acres of forest land were cleared for agriculture, and by the early 1900's most of the virgin forests had been cut for timber. Because turkeys fed largely upon acorns, beech-nuts, and chestnuts, the removal of the mature trees and their replacement by young brushy growth was a staggering blow to the remaining few birds. When the chestnut blighted and this valuable food was lost, the turkey was left literally homeless and foodless. Forest fires, expanding agriculture, and more and more roads added to the inhospitable nature of the remaining forest areas.

But when the turkey was gone, except for a few isolated flocks in the south-central mountains, the sportsmen finally awakened to the fact that this fine game bird was no longer available for sport and for the table. Then came a complete reversal of attitude. All at once sportsmen began to demand all kinds of game protection and the most stringent management measures.

Naturally, the first step in this direction was the establishment of laws and regulations which prevented the unrestricted slaughter of turkeys. Market hunting was outlawed, and seasons and bag limits were established, with penalties provided for violations. As the years passed, these restrictions became tighter, but no limit on the number which could be killed per day or per season was placed on the turkey in Pennsylvania until 1905.

The next step was the creation of many large refuges in the mountains. Areas containing hundreds of acres were enclosed by a single strand of wire and refuge signs posted around the perimeter. Entry was denied all persons except Game Commission officials. Finally, grains were planted in strips and small plots in convenient places in or near the refuges. During severe winters, ear corn was placed in feeders at strategic points to carry the birds thorough emergency periods of deep snow.

Although these measures were believed to be sufficient to restore the turkey, there was only a partial recovery over a limited area in the south-central counties. Something was lacking or something else needed to be done. And this was when research began to play an important role in the wild turkey restoration program.

It was decided that the range was too limited in size to give the bird a real chance to recover. At the same time, there were so few wild birds that it was not practical to attempt to live trap any of these for transfer to other areas. It was decided to propagate some birds artificially for release.

The best thing available at that time was some half-wild

stock which had resulted from a crossing of domestic bronze hens with wild gobblers. The wild turkey farm established in 1929 began business with these semi-domestic turkeys. But they proved to be little better than worthless. Released birds would follow a trail or road to the nearest farmhouse and contentedly take up permanent residence with the tame turkey flock or with the chickens if necessary. They seemed to be content to stay there and be eaten by the farmer or die from the various poultry diseases (especially "blackhead") which they picked up in the barnyard.

So research stepped in to discover how to produce a wild turkey that would stay wild. This endeavor did not follow the scientific pattern set by the modern research method, because in the early 1930's there were no more than a handful of trained wildlife biologists in the country. This early research was carried out by refuge keepers and the propagators assigned to the wild turkey farm. It was pretty much a trial-and-error method, but results were achieved.

The refuge men reasoned that the best way to produce a wild bird was to introduce the blood of genuine wild stock. How to do this was the real problem. A refuge keeper stationed near the Maryland line, a man who had years of experience in hunting turkeys and working with them, eventually came up with an answer. Experimenting, he put some of these half-breed hens in a wire pen out in the mountains early in the spring. The gobblers responded admirably, and every day he could see these old birds "walking the fence," trying to get in with the hens. More experimenting, and he discovered how to let the gobblers in without letting the hens out. The eggs from these breeding areas were taken back to the game farm and hatched. The improved stock was used, in turn, in the propagation areas the following spring and again bred to the wild gobblers.

Within a few years, the Pennsylvania Game Commission was boasting that it had a bird on its game farm which was so wild that it could not be kept on the farm without holding it in covered pens. Where, a few years before, the released birds could hardly be kicked out of the way, when they left the shipping crates, the turkeys now came out of the crates on the wing and commonly flew a half mile before landing. This was the biggest single step in the restoration of the wild turkey in Pennsylvania.

About the time the Game Commission had finally accomplished the task of breeding a truly wild bird, the northern forests in the state were leaving the pole stage and developing into more mature stands of timber. The pole-size trees, from three to six inches in diameter, offered little for any kind of game in terms of food or cover. In fact, these dense stands shaded and crowded out the shrubs which would have provided both cover and food for small game.

But the larger trees—the oaks, the beech, the wild cherries—now were beginning to produce nuts and fruit in large quantities, and the forests were growing into better turkey habitat each year. By 1945, the extensive plantings of the new bird from the game farm began to take hold. A few years later, they had spread from one end of the state to the other, and great concentrations were showing up in some of the north-central counties. As many as 75 to 100 birds in a single flock would appear at the winter feeders during periods of deep snow. As late as 1952, the Game Protectors in that area estimated that, on the average, hunters were not killing more than one bird from each flock.

Today, as more and more hunters are learning of the unparalleled sport offered by these thousands of big, bronze birds, the kill is increasing each year. In 1954 it was estimated that close to 20,000 fell to the hunter's gun. With a daily and season limit of one turkey, this harvest of 20,000 birds means that 20,000 nimrods were fortunate enough to bag a turkey during the one-month season. Surely Pennsylvania has achieved a modern miracle of wildlife restoration in that it can now offer its vast army of sportsmen some of the finest wild turkey hunting on the continent.

This state has proved that this noble bird can be restored to American forests in large numbers. With luck, and patience, hunters in many other states may soon know the feeling of triumph which accompanies this experience of bagging this highly prized trophy in their own forests. The future of wild turkey hunting in North America looks bright.

As a guide to those responsible for wild turkey management in other states, it might be helpful if the factors, which permitted the restoration of the turkey in Pennsylvania, were listed. This should encourage these men to analyze some of the problems or shortcomings of their own range or program in the light of Pennsylvania's experience.

Here are the several basic factors, not necessarily in order of importance:

(1) Pennsylvania has essentially no grazing by any kind of domestic livestock on any of its forests, public or private. Thus, competition for food and interference with reproduction is minimized.

(2) Because of its rather rigorous climate, Pennsylvania has a minimum number of "hillbillys." In states where large

numbers of people live far back in the woods, this adversely affects wild turkey abundance for two reasons. First of all, a large proportion of these people believe in "living off the land," and the illegal kill of turkeys is high throughout the year. Secondly, the location of the cabins in the sags and small valleys and near springs prevent the birds from using many of the best feeding and watering areas and natural crossings. This has the effect of greatly reducing the habitable range.

(3) Pennsylvania has a highly efficient law enforcement set-up which minimizes the illegal kill and reduces the amount of human interference with nesting and brooding during the rearing season.

(4) Pennsylvania is one of the few states which has been able to develop and produce a high quality game farm bird for restocking. Without a bird of this type, all stocking efforts with artificially reared birds are likely to be fruitless.

(5) Pennsylvania's forests in the last 50 to 75 years have progressed from the brush-stage and pole-stage to near mature timber. This has benefited the turkey in two ways. It has permitted them to enjoy greater security against their natural enemies (including man) because they can rely upon their keen sense of sight for safety in the more open forests. And, these mature trees produce food, especially winter foods, in much greater quantity than younger timber.

(6) And finally, the people of Pennsylvania wanted and appreciated the wild turkey as a sporting proposition. Because of this interest, they were willing to pay for a restoration program. And they fostered this program while it was in progress by obeying the game laws and by sanctioning the management efforts.

## Chapter 7:

# Past and Present Management Practices

### Hunting Restrictions

ONE OF THE very first forms of management extended to any game species in North America was some form of harvest restriction. This is known as "passive" management as opposed to "active" management wherein some definite activity is undertaken to preserve or increase the numbers of the animal. Planting food strips or creating forest openings would be examples of active management.

Long before money or personnel were available for management work as we know it today, it was comparatively simple for a state legislature to pass a law placing certain restrictions upon the human enemies of the wild turkey. Oddly enough these laws followed a fairly uniform pattern in several states, although the intensity of restriction was governed somewhat by the density of population and the accessibility of the turkey range. For example, some southern states still permit spring gobbler shooting, but this is considered undesirable in more northern states where hunting pressure is much greater and the entire turkey habitat is crisscrossed with drivable roads.

Most of the very early laws dating back to the first half of the past century merely provided a closed season for a few months during the spring and summer to permit the game to breed in comparative security. No restriction was placed upon method of hunting or numbers to be taken at that time. Later, certain destructive methods of taking large numbers of turkeys were banned. These included the various

99

kinds of traps, in which a whole flock might be caught at one time, snares, set-guns and other non-sporting devices.

By the turn of the century, the various states still lucky enough to have some wild turkeys left began to think of them as a sporting animal for the first time. Prior to that they were merely regarded as another source of meat to be taken in any manner by the individual for food for his family or to sell on the open market. The first step was a ban on market hunting and the sale of game for meat. As populations grew in this country and the number of hunters increased, the desirability of sharing the few wild turkeys which could be killed each year among the hunters was obvious. This was done by placing daily and seasonal bag limits on many kinds of game, including wild turkeys. At first the limits were high, but gradually the number was reduced until today only one turkey can legally be killed during the season in some states.

Restrictions and regulations on wild turkey hunting vary considerably from state to state. In northern states, no spring gobbler shooting is permitted. On the other hand, this is a common practice in the South.

The value of hunting restrictions in wild turkey management seems to be proportional to the degree of hunting pressure. In southern Pennsylvania where the range is easily accessible and pressure is high, the kill may even exceed 50% of the population during some years. Without the strictest control in these areas, the turkey would likely be wiped out rather quickly. In northern Pennsylvania, on the other hand, the annual harvest may be as low as 10% to 20%. Statewide there are probably fifteen turkey hunters for every turkey killed, and this means that, in fairness to all, it would not be desirable to permit some hunters to shoot more than one bird per season.

In some southern states where hunting pressure is much less and large parts of the range may be relatively inaccessible (swamps), the situation is quite different. There the harvest might fall well below 20% if bag-limits and hunting methods were not liberalized. Thus, the use of dogs, the larger daily and seasonal limits, and the spring gobbler seasons may all be permitted in order to achieve a satisfactory harvest. But even with these concessions, this is not always accomplished in many areas.

Hunting restrictions are desirable and necessary in wild turkey management, but should be regulated in accordance with the needs for each state. Where the annual harvest by hunters is only a small part of the annual surplus, restrictions can be lenient. But where hunting pressure is intense, they may have to be very stringent—even to the point of regulating the number of hunters.

## Refuges

A very close relationship exists between the protection provided by refuges and that provided by hunting restrictions. Both are intended to prevent over-cropping of the resident turkey population, and each tends to supplant the other. As an extreme example, if 50% or more of an area were in scattered suitable refuges, it is probable that a good brood stock would survive in spite of the most lenient hunting restrictions. This is, of course, assuming that the refuges would remain inviolate. On the other hand, refuges would have little value where hunting pressure or the annual harvest was kept at a low level by stringent hunting restrictions, or where the area was relatively inaccessible to hunters. In a broad sense, refuges are a type of hunting restriction.

In parts of the South, there are many natural refuges in the form of extensive swamps. To prohibit turkey hunting over large tracts of these swamps would probably have little beneficial effect upon the birds. In most places, it would probably do little more than penalize the hunters unnecessarily. In many parts of the West, the vastness of the wild turkey range and the absence of roads literally make these areas refuges in themselves. Certainly, the cost of establishment and maintenance could not be justified on the grounds of protection to the wild turkey population.

In the East, and in certain parts of the South and West, refuges can be, and are, a valuable management tool. Anywhere gun pressure is high, they become almost a necessity for sustained yields. Refuges have a double purpose, but primarily they are designed to provide sanctuary for harassed flocks during the hunting season. The other purpose is to provide areas wherein the hens may nest and rear their broods unmolested by man.

Just any large tract of land does not necessarily make a good refuge. There are certain essentials which must be fulfilled for them to be successful management units. Dalke, Leopold, and Spencer (1946) list nine requirements for effectiveness in Missouri:

(1) Closure of area to hunting; reduction of trespass, internal traffic, and other disturbances to a minimum.

(2) Control of grazing and, if possible, exclusion of livestock to reduce disturbance and competition with wildlife.

(3) Control of fire, based upon a prevention program out-

side the refuge and backed up, of course, with preparations for suppression.

(4) Maintenance of native turkey stock, where present, without addition of any outside stocks.

(5) Handling of woodlands under a balanced program of silviculture should be practiced on areas where forest production is the major objective, but poorer sites should be maintained in open stands to encourage the growth of a herbaceous and shrubby understory, which produces important wildlife foods and, if desirable, livestock forage. Well-distributed openings, comprising 15% to 25% of the total area, should be maintained. Abandoned ridge-top fields are particularly valuable to wildlife and are usually poor timber sites. These fields, if seeded to grass, not only provide green food for turkeys during the winter, but also improve the range for livestock.

(6) Maintenance of food patches and other supplemental food supplies, when feasible. Food patches are always desirable but become essential only in years when the acorn mast fails, or during periods of deep and continued snow.

(7) Construction of ponds to insure well-distributed permanent water over the management area. Many refuges in Missouri still lack adequate water.

(8) Moderate control of wolves, coyotes, bobcats, and in some cases foxes, primarily to maintain good public relations. Only rarely are the native predators a serious threat to the welfare of turkeys in Missouri.

(9) An intensive public relations program involving personal contacts with all neighboring residents within several miles of the refuge. This should be the basis of the protec-

tion program, supplemented by active enforcement only when necessary.

Naturally, these requirements will vary from state to state, but basically they are sound. In northern forests, water and grazing are seldom problems. The elimination of human interference, particularly hunting, the maintenance of the native flocks without artificial stocking, and the creation and maintenance of forest openings are the most important considerations.

The next questions are: What size should wild turkey refuges be and where should they be located? Size, again, is a variable thing, depending upon many factors. The refuge should be large enough so that the birds feel secure within it and will not tend to cross straight through it when frightened by hunters. Like most game animals, turkeys are quick to realize that the refuge offers security and will readily learn to fly or run to it when in danger. But if too small, it is difficult for them to recognize its existence, because they are unlikely to stay within its boundaries long enough to learn its protective value.

Refuge size will vary with the intended purpose. If turkeys are abundant, they may need these sanctuaries for little more than temporary protection during the hunting season. If refuges are too large or if there are too many, they may actually prevent a satisfactory harvest of the birds. Thus, in regions where the wild turkey population is high, refuges of from 500 to 2,000 acres may be very adequate, and not more than 5% of the managed area need to be closed to hunting.

Where an attempt is being made to establish wild turkeys on range where they have not existed for many years, or where a remnant population is being carefully fostered, larger refuges are desirable. These may be as large as 5,000 to 10,000 acres and even as large as 50,000 to 300,000 acres in the West. The idea here is to keep a large part of the population inside the refuge during the entire year to prevent losses from poaching and hunting. Forests openings, food plots, winter feeders in the North, and other management measures all tend to keep the birds inside.

Where should refuges be established? If turkeys are already present, they should encompass the home range of one or more resident flocks. If a refuge is established simultaneously with a new stocking program, it should contain the minimum essentials of wild turkey habitat—food, water, forest openings, and mature timber. At best this is a risky proposition, because the game manager has no assurance that the area he picks as a refuge will be adopted by the introduced turkeys. It appears to be safest to put up the refuge wire after the birds have selected their own living quarters.

The most satisfactory types of refuge boundary line marker appears to be a single strand of number nine round wire tacked to trees or stakes at about waist height. Metal signs should be hung from this wire at about 50 yard intervals. These commonly read "STATE GAME REFUGE" or some other similar designation. Between these metal signs at intervals of 100 yards or more, paper signs may be placed on board backing and nailed to the trees from which the wire is suspended. These paper signs list the regulations and penalties governing trespassing on the area. It is usually necessary to brush out a 10 or 15 foot line outside the wire whenever roads or trails are not used as outside boundaries.

Intermittent patrol and strict law enforcement are usually necessary to keep the refuge area inviolate. In addition, education on a local and state level is very desirable, so that the hunters will understand the purpose of the sanctuaries and respect the single strand of wire wherever they may encounter it.

## Predator Control

The simple fact that some animals kill and eat other animals has caused more heated arguments and controversy than nearly any other subject pertaining to the conservation or management of wildlife. The hunter sees a hawk or a fox kill a piece of game, and he is indignant. The professional wildlife manager may witness the same incident and shrug his shoulders. Or he may even experience a feeling of satisfaction, because in some cases predation can actually be beneficial to game and to the hunter.

Obviously, there are reasons why many hunters and game managers differ in their opinions about predation. The hunter sees the misdeed committed, and assumes that the piece of game, if it had not been killed, would have been there for the hunting season in the fall. Then he is likely to sit down with pencil and paper and figure out the losses mathematically. He decides that the fox, for example, kills a certain number of game animals each week. He then multiplies this number by 52 and gets the total game killed by one fox in a year. This figure is then multiplied by his estimated number of foxes, and the result is usually an astronomical figure. He thinks how wonderful hunting would be if all this extra game were available, and decides that the only salvation is in killing predators. And almost invariably he and his associates end up by insisting that the State Game Department put a bounty on the offending animals. Usually the suggested list of animals to be bountied includes everything from crows and oppossums to wolves and bobcats.

The argument seems logical enough at first glance. There is no question but that the meat eaters do kill a lot of game during a year's time, and it would seem that this would certainly have a real effect upon the hunting bag. And if a good part of the predators were killed, the hunters would have that much more sport during the hunting season. But it is not nearly so simple as that. There are several reasons why predation is not always as serious as it seems and why predator control programs most often fail to produce the intended results.

Scattered observations of kills by predators are not a reliable index of damage done to game populations. Food habits studies through the careful examination of the remains found in stomachs, pellets, or droppings are much more reliable, but even these have their limitations. Stomachs are most reliable. Pellets which are formed of undigested bones, hair, and feathers in the stomachs of hawks and owls and later regurgitated, are also reliable. Scats, which are the droppings of carnivorous mammals such as foxes, bobcats, raccoons, etc. are used to determine food habits, but are the most difficult to analyze.

To be useful and acceptable as an indication of the diet of a predator, the analysis work must be done by an expert. It takes plenty of training and experience for a technician to be able to look at the contents of a stomach, pellet, or scat and be able to identify all of the items correctly. Then oftentimes the food found does not represent the true diet of the animal. Some things are killed and not eaten. Foxes will regularly discard shrews, moles, weasels, skunks, opossums, and perhaps others unless they are extremely hungry. Or a fox, mink, weasel, or many other predators may kill several game birds at one time or in one night, but only eat a part of one or two. Raids on chicken houses provide a good example of this.

On the other hand predators often eat animals they have not killed. Poultry and other dead domestic animals are often thrown out in the farmer's fields or on the town "dump" and gathered up by predators. The appearance of adult game birds and mammals usually is greater during and just after the hunting season. This is because the meat eating animals gather up the wounded and dead game left by the hunters. Then there are other thousands of prey animals killed on the highways which may eventually be eaten. All of this carrion can put some predators in a bad light if the true facts are not known.

One of the most serious criticisms of predator food habits studies is that often the figures from a series of stomachs, pellets, or scats collected during one or two seasons of the year are given as representing the typical diet of the animal. For many years, almost all of the food analyses for furbearers were made from stomachs taken during the fall and winter when these animals were being trapped for their fur. But these stomachs told nothing about what damage the furbearers were doing to nests and eggs of game birds or the young of any game species. Nor did they reveal how many nests of young mice and other destructive rodents were being dug out by skunks and other ground predators.

The board-winged hawk which is ordinarily considered one of the most beneficial hawks can be used to illustrate the great seasonal variation in diet. In the fall the broadwing lives almost entirely on large grasshoppers, katydids, caterpillars, and some mice, moles, and other small items. And, except for a brief period when nesting, this hawk continues to eat items of this kind. But a study of nesting broadwings in good ruffed grouse country showed that they were killing a large number of grouse chicks to feed their fledglings. A study made during these few weeks only might cause the broadwing to be rated as a destructive hawk. Throughout the rest of the year, it would be classified as definitely beneficial to farmers and sportsmen alike. The crow is another bird which is damned by the sportsman as being a serious predator, but this is only for a few weeks during spring and summer when they destroy the eggs of game birds and the young of rabbits and perhaps other game animals. The rest of the year, it does little more than compete with ringnecks and quail for corn and other grain left in the farmer's fields.

The same argument can be used against food habit studies made for one year only. The next year, or five years later, the diet of the same predator, for the same season and place may be much different. Many kinds of prey animals, such as grouse, snowshoe hares, mice, and others, are cyclic and may fluctuate greatly in numbers over a period of years. All prey animal populations respond to periods of drought, excessive rainfall, deep snows, and other weather factors so that they may be much more abundant one year than the next. Mice are the staple diet of many hawks, owls, and furbearers. When these small animals are scarce, predators may be forced to turn to larger prey, such as game, to keep alive.

When mice again become abundant, game may be relatively safe.

And finally, the variations between the diets of the same predator from different localities may be just as pronounced as they are between seasons or between years. Predators living in the forest areas of a state could hardly be expected to consume the same food as those found on open farmland. Ruffed grouse and wild turkeys might be present in the forest food items but unlikely in the farm diet. Conversely, ringnecked pheasants and bobwhite quail would not be found with any regularity in predator stomachs from the deep forest areas.

Within certain limits, availability, above all else, governs the diet of most North American predatory animals found outside of the Arctic. Most meat-eating animals are opportunists, and if one prey item does not occur in fair abundance or is not easily captured, it will be replaced on the diet list by other more readily available prey species, or even by nonprey items such as carrion or vegetable foods. It is only logical that when a certain prey item is abundant, its natural enemies are afforded more opportunities to kill than when the animal occurs only sparsely.

All of the foregoing has been presented in an attempt to convince the reader that the true relationship between a particular predator and a certain prey animal cannot be decided from a few scattered observations nor from a few, nor a few hundred, examinations of predator stomachs, pellets, or scats. For example, if a series of bobcat stomachs were examined and evidence was found to indicate that several wild turkeys had been killed and eaten, the following information would be necessary before a reasonably correct interpretation of this relationship could be made: How abundant or how scarce were wild turkeys in the area where the bobcats were taken? How abundant or how scarce were bobcats in this same area? How many other kinds of predators were also killing wild turkeys and how abundant or scarce were each? What other prey animals, such as mice, other rodents, rabbits, and hares, were present on the area to act as "buffers" for the wild turkey, and how abundant or scarce were each of these? And finally, what effect did unusual weather, the physical condition of the birds, the amount of protective cover, the season of the year, and the number of game-farm turkeys stocked have on the availability of these birds to the bobcat? From all this, it is obvious that it takes a well trained wildlife biologist to decide whether the bobcat is a threat to the wild turkey in that particular area and whether reduction of the bobcat population would actually benefit the turkeys and the hunters.

And now to get down to some basic facts about the predator control controversy.

Almost all animal populations, generally speaking, maintain a certain status quo. If this were not true, they would tend to increase to unbelievable numbers or decrease to a dangerous low or complete extermination in a very few years. This means that, unless a species is increasing or decreasing at a rapid rate, for every individual born during a year one must die before the next breeding season. In Pennsylvania, it is believed that about four million cottontails on the average survive the winter and are present at the beginning of the breeding season. The approximately two million females are capable of producing, and almost certainly do produce, somewhere between twenty and forty million young between early spring and early fall. Even though the hunting season kill recently has rarely gone over two to three million (officially estimated at about one and one-half to two millions), the number of breeders the following spring is again at about four millions. This means that somewhere between twenty and forty million rabbits die or get killed from all causes in a single year.

The same turnover is essentially true for wild turkeys and other game species. Generally speaking, predators live on this annual surplus, and they seldom cause a serious reduction in succeeding breeding populations. The law of diminishing returns works just as well for the predators as it does for human hunters. When a kind of prey is abundant, both the animal and the human hunter are able to make kills with some regularity. But as the prey becomes increasingly scarce, it is more and more difficult for either to be successful. When the prey reaches a certain low point, the predator, and often the hunter, will turn to other kinds of game or prey which are more abundant and easier to capture. Except under the most unusual circumstances, no predator, except man, will ever exterminate a prey species.

The term "predator" does not necessarily denote a destructive animal anyway. Some of the most beneficial animals in terms of man's economy are predators. A classical example of this is given by Stoddard in his book, *The Bobwhite Quail*. He discovered that cotton rats were responsible for destroying more bobwhite nests than any other animal. These field rats ate the bobwhite eggs and caused tremendous losses when abundant. Stoddard also found that the marsh hawk was living largely on these cotton rats, and was keeping their numbers reduced to a tolerance level. Even though the marsh hawk occasionally killed and ate a quail, it was actually very beneficial to this small game bird because it removed a large number of its natural enemies.

In New York, a study of predator relationships on a duck marsh revealed a like situation. The marsh contained a good number of nesting ducks and some snapping turtles. The snappers laid their eggs in the sand of the beaches, but most of these were dug out and destroyed by the large population of skunks. Skunk fur became much in demand and was bringing a high price, so the trappers of the area reduced their numbers greatly. Soon the marsh was overrun with snappers, and a mother duck was lucky to bring more than one or two of her brood to maturity. The large turtle grasped a foot of the young ducklings and pulled it under and devoured it. After several years of duck scarcity on the marsh, skunk fur dropped greatly in price and the trappers turned to more profitable furbearers. Soon the skunks recovered, ate the snapper eggs on the beaches, and before long the duck hunting was good once again. This is still another case of one predator controlling another.

There are even more direct values. Barn owls destroy millions of mice and barn rats every year. In this manner, they save hundreds of thousands of dollars worth of field crops and stored grain and feed for the farmers. One barn owl does more good than a dozen farm cats.

There are many, many more examples, but just a few are mentioned to show that indiscriminate killing of all predators is not wise.

Another thing, the number of predators is important. No matter how destructive an animal may be, it can do little real harm unless it occurs in some quantity. For example, the goshawk is reputed to kill fifty grouse a year in Canada. In some parts of that country, they are quite abundant and undoubtedly do kill many grouse. But on the other hand these large hawks are very scarce in Pennsylvania, Maryland, West Virginia and other states at the southern tip of its range. Even though individually they are just as destructive as in Canada, the handful found in these states could do no real damage to the total number of grouse. To the contrary, a predator which is only slightly harmful individually can do tremendous damage if it occurs in great numbers. Chipmunks, playfully or otherwise, are known to roll grouse eggs out of nests, often without eating them. Although a single chipmunk may only remove one or two eggs all spring, this misdeed if multiplied by the millions which live in many forested areas could easily mean the difference between a good hatch and a poor one. Therefore, a predatory species should not be judged on what a single individual does, but rather on the total effect of all the individuals combined upon the prey population.

In fact, this can be said just as effectively in reverse. Most of the disagreement about the predator problem arises from the fact that those who favor predator control are thinking in terms of *individual* animals lost, while most of those who oppose control, or believe it is not necessary, are thinking in terms of *species* or *population* survival. It does seem useless to control predators and perhaps save additional game animals if the hunters are not adequately harvesting the annual surplus anyway. Many hunters in the eastern states ask that the Game Department put a bounty on foxes or horned owls because they are killing cottontails which the hunters want to kill in season. And yet, rabbit studies have shown, time and time again, that less than 20% of the rabbits are harvested even on the most heavily hunted regions. Over large areas, the kill may be as low as 10% or less. What value is predator control under those circumstances?

A point which hunters will find difficult to believe is that predation can actually be beneficial to wildlife and, in turn, to the hunters themselves. One of the most important effects of predation on game animals is what is called the "sanitation effect" by game managers. In any game population there are always diseased, injured, and unfit animals which should be eliminated. The sick animal should be killed and eaten so that it will not spread disease to other game animals. This certainly contributes to the health of the total population and may be essential to the survival of a species in some cases.

Perhaps just as important is the removal of the unwary, slow, and stupid individuals. In this way game retains the sporting qualities of strength and wildness which make hunting so worthwhile. Predation is nature's way of accomplishing the same end as culling, sanitation, and selective breeding do for tame flocks and herds. Surely, any right thinking hunter will agree that this is a desirable service.

Along this same line, there is plenty of evidence that predators are necessary for the well-being and even survival of certain game species. For example, the wild turkey, if undisturbed, will begin to nest in April and will usually hatch in late May or early June. The devastating effect of a cold, rainy spell at this time has already been explained. Suppose *all* turkey nests hatched within a two week period year after year, and just by coincidence the hatching dates fell during a cold, wet spell for about two or three years in a row. We would be out of turkeys! But nest predators, such as crows, skunks, raccoons, and others destroy a part of the first eggs, and a third or more of the hens may have to re-nest. Sometimes this third produces the major part of the birds found in hunting season, because the main hatch was a failure.

There are other benefits, too. Some things like deer, rabbits, snowshoe hares, and other game animals can increase very rapidly to a point where they outgrow their food supply. Then the hunters are the people who suffer, because the game decreases to a very low point until the range has time to recover, and this sometimes takes many years. The famous Kaibab deer herd is one example. This herd had almost no natural enemies and was definitely underhunted. In a very few years it increased so rapidly that almost all natural forage was destroyed. Then came the crash. Soon there was only a handful left compared to the former great numbers. And it took about twenty-five to thirty years for the range to recover somewhat.

Because the extent of predation usually increases as the number of prey animals increases, predators may prevent this disastrous overpopulation in many instances. Of course, this applies only where the hunters themselves cannot keep the game under control. But even in eastern states, with plenty of hunters, deer have been permitted to ruin their food supply where the "Buck Law" prevented a regular harvest of antlerless deer.

And finally, predators may "soften" the effect of game cycles. Charles Elton, the famed British wildlife scientist, describes an instance of this:

"In Norway the willow grouse in earlier years used to

multiply periodically and every three or four years every sportsman got a fine bag. After these good years the grouse, as they did in America, died off from disease because they had become so populous. At the same time, the Norwegians had a great drive to wipe out birds and animals of prey: eagles, foxes, martens, and other fur animals. As the predatory birds and mammals have become scarcer, it has been noticed that the epidemics among willow grouse have become increasingly worse. Instead of more and better willow-grouse populations having been produced by supposed protection through widespread destruction of predators, the stock of these birds has become progressively more decreased.

"It was suggested that the reason for this great mortality was this: when a grouse became sick with coccidiosis, it weakened and flew less readily and was thus easier to catch. As a result, in the old days the predators used to catch the sick birds more readily than the healthy birds and so prevented disease from becoming too severe, except after the birds had become very abundant."

Then predators also remove countless thousands of mice, red squirrels, chipmunks, gophers, rats, and other rodents which compete with game for food and often destroy eggs and young. In the wild turkey forests, mice and members of the squirrel family eat tons of nuts, seeds, berries, and other foods which would be available to the wild turkeys and other game if it were not for these small animals. The hawks, owls, and furbearers do the game a real favor in reducing the numbers of these rodents.

But suppose in spite of the arguments presented, that game departments or sportsmen still insist in predator control.

Does it often accomplish anything worthwhile for the hunters? Could more have been accomplished with the same amount of money by undertaking some other type of game management effort? Does the ordinary kind of predator control actually reduce the degree of predation particularly?

Many attempts have been made to determine the value of predator control for different game species. So far, almost all of these demonstrations have failed for one or two reasons. The first is that *it is almost impossible to control predators over a large area with a reasonable amount of manpower and money*. And the second reason is that it has been proved again and again that *a substantial reduction of predators does not necessarily mean reduced predator pressure!*

One of the best examples of this was a study in Texas on a 960 acre tract. In 1942, coyotes destroyed 52% of the quail nests found on the area. A vigorous predator control program removed 632 coyotes and 35 bobcats on and immediately surrounding the study area. The following spring the coyotes, now relatively scarce, destroyed 56% of the bobwhite nests found.

Moderate to severe reduction of a particular predator may merely mean that the surviving individual will live better. That is, each will kill and eat more because it has more opportunity than before when competition was high. Or other predatory species may step in and take over for those which were killed. This is in accordance with the idea that, when a game species is abundant on an area, a certain surplus number is particularly vulnerable to predators. As this surplus is removed, the remaining birds or mammals become harder and harder to catch—the old law of diminishing returns again. So in the final analysis, it appears that a certain number of turkeys, or quail, or cottontails, or anything else on an area are relatively secure, but all over that number are living precariously. A few predators can eliminate this extra game almost as easily as a larger number. Conversely, once this surplus has been removed the remainder appear to be reasonably secure whether there are many or a few predators.

The cost of attempted control of predators runs exceedingly high. The bounty system has failed repeatedly to reduce predators to a control level, and usually the annual surplus is all that is removed. This partial reduction is considered a waste of money for the reason just explained—those left can just as effectively kill the surplus game animals as the original number. In spite of a constant high bounty on foxes in Pennsylvania since 1915, there are as many or more today than formerly. As many as fifty thousand foxes may be bountied in a single year, but this is probably only 30% to 40% of the total foxes in the State. With litters of from 5 to 9, or even more, recovery is very rapid.

Besides being usually ineffective in controlling predator populations, there are other objections to bounty systems. Many beneficial or harmless species are killed in mistake for those on the bounty list. This is especially true of hawks and owls. Traps and other devices are also likely to be non-selective. Bounty systems are exceedingly inefficient because many of the animals sent in for the reward would have been killed anyway. In Pennsylvania it was found that 57% of the claimants sending in foxes for bounty had killed only one fox during the year. Most of these were taken accidentally or incidentally and would have been killed whether a bounty was paid or not. Fifty-nine per cent of the horned owls, about 75% of the weasels, and all goshawks submitted for bounty in Pennsylvania would have been killed anyway. This means that hundreds of thousands of dollars have been paid out for nothing!

And finally, every bounty is accompanied with a certain amount of fraud. Unless under the strictest supervision, fraudulent claims can destroy any possible value of the system.

Certain game management efforts can partially nullify the effects of predation. It has already been mentioned that a certain portion of a game population seems to be relatively safe from predators. This percentage can be increased by habitat improvement. Wildlife managers agree that without adequate protective cover, small game is susceptible to heavy predation. Thus, the provision of the proper kinds of vegetative growth is an important means of combatting the effects of predation. The new cover must be of the proper kind and must be established in the proper places. Heavy cover is of little value if small game species must leave it and expose themselves in the open in order to feed. The food, roosting sites, and nesting sites must be favorably located in relation to the protective cover if game is going to benefit from this kind of management work.

Before leaving the subject of predator control, something should be said about the effects of predator reduction on wild turkey populations. Very few attempts have been made deliberately to benefit turkeys in this manner, and especially where an effort has been made to measure the results. One investigator reported some favorable results after removing 217 bobcats and 199 gray foxes in two years on the 100,000 acre Chattahoochee National Forest in northern Georgia. Very intense coyote control in the King Ranch in Texas was credited with permitting a pronounced increase in turkeys there.

It appears from a study of many predator control campaigns that those most likely to succeed are the ones involving large predators such as mountain lions, wolves, coyotes, bobcats, etc., and large prey animals like deer, antelope, moose, and others. This is logical when analyzed. For one thing, these large animals seldom reach the abundance of the smaller predators—skunks, opossums, raccoons, foxes, weasels, hawks, owls, etc. And the large prey animals seldom reach the abundance of the smaller prey animals— cottontails, snowshoe hares, other rabbits, squirrels, grouse, pheasants, quail, etc. Consequently, when a large predator kills a large prey animal, it has much more effect upon the total population than when a small predator kills a small prey animal. For the same reason, when a large predator is killed, this is much more likely to be beneficial to the prey species than when a small predator is killed. Also, animals like deer, antelope and other big game have fewer natural enemies than rabbits, quail, and other small animals. And sometimes it is just as easy, or maybe easier, to kill a hundred coyotes as it is to kill a hundred sharpshinned hawks which may be preying on quail.

In summary, it would seem that if important losses are occurring to adult wild turkeys, predator control may pay off in some instances. This would seldom involve anything except bobcats, coyotes, and other predators of similar or larger size. If the losses are principally of eggs or poults to small predators, then the results of control would be exceedingly doubtful, simply because it is almost impossible to reduce their numbers to a control level. This is especially true where domestic animals might be endangered by stringent methods (poison, etc.). And except on small, intensively managed areas, the cost of such a program would be completely prohibitive.

If predator control is believed advisable by the owners or members of a hunting club, the local wildlife authorities should be consulted before any program is initiated. In most states, certain devices or materials are illegal. For example, poisons and poison gases cannot be used freely in most states, and these substances should never be used except by experts or under the direction of experts. Poisons such as 1080, cyanide, and others may be as dangerous to the amateur user as to the predators. And all poisons are potentially dangerous to livestock and even humans. A few valuable dogs or other pets lost in the neighborhood can put a sportsmen's club in a bad light.

In the West where the population is sparse, poisons and coyote-getters may be valuable tools in wild turkey management, but these can be used safely in very few places in the East and South. The skilled trapper is the safest and best bet here. Of course, anytime predators such as foxes, bobcats, and raccoons can be removed by hunters with hounds, this is the ideal way because these men are enjoying some fine recreation at the same time. Crows, horned owls, and foxes can be called in and shot, thus providing some more great sport. This is probably the ideal way for a club to solve its predator problem. Quite often predator hunting is better all-around recreation than game hunting. Why not try it?

## Stocking of Farm-Reared Wild Turkeys

Once in a long while a game species will spread over large areas of its own accord. The history of Pennsylvania's deer herd bears out this fact. From a mere handful in the south-central part of the State, the whitetail expanded in all directions, finally populating every county in the State and eventually pushing over into Ohio, southern New York, New Jersey, and probably Maryland and Delaware. But this is an unusual occurrence. Usually game is introduced into new range by stocking a number of individuals. Depending upon the kind, this may be a few pairs, a few dozen, or many thousands.

Game managers are generally agreed that the finest stock for new introductions is wild-trapped game, particularly from regions of similar latitude, climate, topography, vegetation, etc. Unfortunately, these exacting requirements are seldom met except when a state may be carrying on its own trapping and transfer program. In recent years, however, there has been splendid cooperation between certain states and provinces, and wild turkeys and other game have been traded back and forth with extremely gratifying results. Montana, Wyoming, and South Dakota have received wild-trapped Merriam's turkeys from Colorado and New Mexico. Oklahoma has been stocking wild-trapped Rio Grande turkeys from Texas. Many of these releases have succeeded beyond all expectations. South Dakota had its first Merriam's turkey season in the history of the State during 1954, all from a few birds stocked between 1948 and 1952.

In the East, wild trapped birds from Florida and probably other southern states have been used for stocking in the wild and for improving the quality of breeders on game farms.

But for the most part, stocking has been done with wild turkeys reared on game farms. Many states have had wild turkey farms of their own during the past twenty-five years and a handful of these still exist. Generally speaking these propagation plants have not been successful. For one thing, stock reared on most state wild turkey farms during the 1930's and early 1940's was of questionable value. These hybrid birds, a cross between wild and domestic strains, lacked the wildness and characteristics of self-preservation necessary for survival. Many states tried large numbers of these birds over a period of years, and dropped the whole idea after repeated failures. Today a good number of wild-life officials still believe that the wild turkey cannot prosper in their states, based upon the results of these early plantings. Present-day, top-quality farm-reared stock or wild-trapped birds might completely reverse these early experiences.

Through the regular addition of wild blood and by careful selection of brood stock, some state wild turkey farms and private breeders are producing birds capable of establishing themselves in many areas not now occupied. Pennsylvania's experience with game farm wild turkeys is a real success story already related in an earlier chapter. With birds reared on its single turkey farm, this state was able to extend the range of the turkey from 3 million acres to 13 million acres in a little over ten years. Without the wild blood bred into the game farm hens by means of the mountain propagation areas already described, this accomplishment surely never would have been possible.

But today as always, some private breeders, and probably some states, still do not have high quality birds. Sportsmen and game managers alike should be sure of the stock they buy or raise before wasting a lot of money and effort on a stocking program actually doomed to failure before it begins.

Now let's look at stocking in general. Biologically speaking there are only two good reasons for this practice: (1) To introduce an animal which has never occurred in the area, or to reestablish an animal which was present at one time but disappeared for one reason or another; and (2) to supplement a breeding population which is so low that it is unable to propagate rapidly enough to maintain a satisfactory surplus for hunting.

The first reason is certainly legitimate, if wildlife officials are convinced that the animal (for example, the wild turkey) will succeed and that it will be a desirable addition to the fauna of the area. The second reason is far more open to question. There is a term commonly used by game men called "carrying capacity." This simply means that any particular area of land can support just so many pieces of game, in the same way that a pasture or an acreage of grassland can support just so many head of cattle or sheep. Usually carrying capacity is used in reference to a single game species. In the case of the wild turkey, carrying capacity may be controlled, limited, or modified by such things as food, size of range, age and composition of the vegetation, predation, legal and illegal hunting, weather (particularly deep snows), disease, and probably other lesser prominent factors.

This capacity of the land cannot be increased normally

unless there is some change in the above-mentioned controls. For example, through education or strict law enforcement, or both, the amount of illegal killing might be drastically reduced. This could immediately affect the carrying capacity. Or, as happened in Pennsylvania, the young brush or pole stage forests might approach maturity and fulfill the needs of the bird in terms of food and cover. This might conceivably change the carrying capacity from near zero to a very satisfactory level within a decade or two. The rule then governing supplemental stocking is that this is practical only when the wild turkey population is believed to be below an increasing carrying capacity. But even this is questionable, because normally the native stock will respond to the improved environment and rapidly increase of its own accord. If the holding capacity is not increased, either naturally or artificially, then the additions of more breeding stock will produce no results. If wild birds are already present, they will normally respond to the improved conditions and increase their numbers to the new carrying capacity level.

Now what are the objections to the stocking of artificially propagated wild turkeys when the above conditions do not exist? The most obvious one has already been stated. It just does no good. That is, it rarely does much to increase the resident population of native birds and contributes little if anything to the hunter's bag. Money spent for this purpose by game departments is being poured down the rat hole, except for a very dubious public relations value. Sportmen's clubs cannot even claim this much return, except as it might satisfy the membership because they appear to be doing something worthwhile.

Fall stocking of young gobblers for the gun also falls into this category. If these birds are put out at ten to twelve weeks of age in late summer or early fall (a couple months or more before the hunting season), the hunting take will probably be no better than 10%, perhaps much less. The return will be considerably better if the gobblers are planted immediately before the season or during the season. Under heavy hunting pressure, as high as 30% to 50% may be killed. But because it takes 4, 5, or even more dollars to hold one of these gobblers on a state game farm until late fall, stocking for the gun is an exceedingly costly proposition. Because most state small game licenses only cost from 2 to 5 dollars, game departments generally cannot afford to spend sufficient money for this purpose to insure a worthwhile harvest by the hunters. In states where this is done, it is doubtful whether more than one turkey for each 500 to 1,000 licensed hunters is killed. This is hardly practical wildlife management!

Another strong argument against the fall stocking of young gobblers in areas where native birds already exist is that, if some of these do survive, they may eventually breed with wild hens. If this game farm stock is not top quality, the young poults produced by this mating will almost certainly be of poorer quality then those from a truly wild mating. Of course, the same argument holds just as well for spring stocking of game farm hens of unproven quality.

Another serious objection to the stocking of farm-reared wild turkeys is that they may carry dangerous diseases to the wild population. Any wild turkey farm, even with maximum effort toward sanitation and medication, has its fair share of disease. Blackhead, coccidiosis, and a whole series of others are invariably present. This means that these same diseases are carried with this stock into the forests to pollute the soil and sometimes to infect wild birds directly through close contact. Because diseases are known to be highly significant in the management of native wild turkeys, this repeated infection from game farm stock can be a very serious matter.

And finally, there is a rather obscure objection. Game farm birds lack the characteristics of self-protection possessed by wild birds simply because they have never had a mother to train them. For example, the appearance of a predator will put the wild bird instantly upon the alert and it will respond to the situation by doing something about escaping. On the other hand, the newly released farm-reared bird is likely to show little more than idle curiosity when a predator appears, and this can often be a fatal mistake.

When predators find these comparatively stupid, unwary birds in the forests, they have little trouble making a kill. This encourages them to try again. After a few successful attempts, the individual fox, owl, bobcat, or other predator becomes a confirmed turkey killer and then begins to stalk the wild birds. Without this experience provided by the artificially reared turkeys, few of these would ever have the opportunity to develop a taste for turkey meat. So this is still another way in which the stocking of game farm birds is likely to jeopardize the precious native turkeys.

But stocking can be exceedingly desirable under certain conditions, and here are some suggestions as to how, where, and at what time of year it should be done. When actually in the process of releasing birds from the shipping crates, a rough estimate of their quality can be made. The best stock will emerge flying and should fly from a hundred yards to a half-mile before lighting on the ground or in a tree. Beware of turkeys which step out of the crates and begin feeding or in other ways appear to ignore the presence of the man behind the crate. Of course, good judgment should temper any decision. A bird cannot fly well if its feathers are broken or if it has been cramped too long in a small crate. However, it should make a desperate attempt to get as far away as possible as quickly as possible.

There appears to be little advantage in a "quiet" release, because the birds quickly call together and form a flock anyway. With good wild birds, it is very difficult to have them walk out of a crate and wander off as a group. Also, there appears to be little advantage of holding game farm birds in enclosures in the forest for a time before releasing them merely by opening the gate. Unless elaborate precautions are taken to protect the birds against predators, a large part or all of them may be killed very quickly right inside the pen. The "acclimatizing" effect of the pen is hardly worth the effort or the risk.

Spring stocking of wild turkeys should always be made in the immediate vicinity of a forest opening of some size, or near the forest edge some distance from any farms with ranging poultry. If turkeys are put down in the deep forest, they are likely to wander for many miles searching for openings. While traveling in this manner, they neglect to feed properly and may become weak and emaciated within two or three weeks. Then they become susceptible to diseases, or to predation, and a part of the flock may be lost.

Now when should releases be made? It is customary at

the present time for nine to ten month old turkeys to be stocked in the spring, usually in March in the more northern states. This has the disadvantage of placing birds into a strange environment when natural food is scarcest, and just a month or less before nesting begins. Because of the abrupt change in nutrition, the loss of weight, and constant harassment by predators, it is probable that only a small percentage of these birds nest successfully the first year. On the other hand, birds released immediately following the fall hunting season would have four months for adjustment to living in the wild and would not receive the shock experienced by March-released birds just prior to the laying season. The disadvantage of late fall releases is obvious. There is bound to be some loss to this stock over winter. But, it is believed that this mortality is offset by the much greater reproduction expected from the surviving hens the following spring. This same principle probably holds true for ring-necked pheasants as well.

As stated before, the return from young gobblers stocked for the gun is greatest when these birds are put out just before and during the hunting season. A natural objection to this is that these newly released gobblers are not wild and do not possess the characteristics which provide real sport for the hunter. But if they are turned loose in late summer or early fall, the survival until hunting season is usually so poor that the venture is economically unsound. In fact, where native turkeys are reasonably abundant, the most efficient way to deal with the surplus gobblers from a state game farm may be to dispose of them as day-old poults. At this time they can be sexed out quite readily, and their elimination would completely remove the need for this expensive and unrewarding management effort.

Long and costly experience by many states indicates that releases of birds under ten weeks of age is an almost complete waste. Most game farm stock is wildest at about ten weeks, but still relatively insecure against smaller predators such as hawks, owls, foxes, weasels, minks, and many others. At fourteen to sixteen weeks, they are nearly mature and have attained a comparative immunity to smaller predators. But they are now less wild, and much additional money has been used up in feeding them during the extra weeks. Additional experimentation needs to be done to determine the most effective and efficient time for releasing brood stock. This work is now underway in one or more states.

### Forest Management

*Cover.* When one speaks of *cover* for wild turkeys, the word has a far different meaning than it does when it is used in reference to cover for cottontails, quail, ruffed grouse, snowshoe hares, deer, and some other game species. The kinds of game named need plenty of undegrowth, particularly brush and herbaceous vegetation, for best results. Deer need low brushy growth for food. Rabbits, snowshoes, bobwhites, and ruffed grouse need low growth of various kinds for both food and protection. And this protection can be against severe weather as well as against predators.

On the other hand, wild turkeys, squirrels, and bears prefer, and evidently require, mature timber for prosperity. Wild turkeys and bears can get along without underbrush protection against predators, because of their size, and because the wild turkey can fly into the trees when danger threatens from the ground. In fact, the turkey is safer when it relies upon its extraordinary eyesight rather than upon the dubious protection of thick vegetation. This is because it does not normally "freeze" and depend upon protective coloration to save its skin as in the case of the cottontail, the bobwhite, and the ruffed grouse. The squirrel depends upon popping into a hole in the trunk or limbs of the larger trees or into leaf nests for escaping its enemies.

So *cover* for the wild turkey means that a good proportion of the timber should be mature and should be hardwoods. Large pure stands of pines or other conifers do not provide sufficient year-round food to hold turkeys successfully. Small stands of conifers intermixed with hardwoods are acceptable, especially for roosting cover during severe weather. At least 10% of the forest should be in grassy openings, and this may be increased to as high as 50% or more if these openings are not used extensively by humans or their livestock. Usually when a high percentage of the land is cleared, these clearings are used for raising farm crops, for grazing, or for rural dwellings. This all means human interference, and if there is sufficient open land and consequently a large amount of human interference, the range may become untenable for wild turkeys. But, if the openings are natural or abandoned, then as much as 50% of the range or more can be non-forested without adversely affecting the birds. The main thing to remember is that these openings must be scattered throughout the timbered areas so that the turkeys on any portion of the tract do not have to travel far in any direction without finding one or more.

Successful nesting and rearing is largely based upon the presence of these scattered openings.

Basically then, the wild turkey manager has two major obligations to fulfill on the forest lands under his control: (1) to maintain the area in timber sufficiently mature to produce mast in quantity; and (2) to produce and maintain grassy openings throughout the forest, preferably on some kind of a grid pattern.

The first obligation can best be fulfilled by a carefully regulated harvest of the timber on a *selection cutting* basis. By removing only those trees which have fully matured, the forest will remain permanently in a highly productive fruiting stage. This type of cutting is also in accord with good forestry practices. The only time foresters and wild turkey managers are likely to disagree about cutting practices on non-timber sites is concerning the disposition of "wolf" trees. These are mature or over-mature trees which are hollow or otherwise of no particular value for saw timber. These trees are oftentimes the best seed producers and naturally the wildlifer wants to save them. The forester usually wants to cut them because they shade out the young trees growing close-by.

In regions where a large part of the forest is managed for pulpwood for the paper industry, clear cutting is the general practice. This is not desirable in terms of turkey management, but it really does not matter particularly because pulp timber will rarely produce wild turkeys anyway. But clear cutting in saw timber is discouraged unless it is done in small parcels well scattered throughout the total forest.

The second objective of forest management for wild

turkeys is more difficult to attain. If the clearings are not already present, it may be a real problem to get permission to remove timber just to create openings on lands not owned by state game departments. But where it is possible to go ahead with this work, the results can be accomplished in several ways. The best way is to cut the trees from the proposed opening and market them in the most economical manner—for sawlogs, pulp, chemical wood, fire wood, etc. Sometimes there will be no ready market, or the product may be so far back in the forest and so inaccessible that it cannot be marketed economically. In this case, the trees can be cut, bulldozed, or killed with a herbicide.

Bulldozing is one of the most efficient ways of creating grassy openings. This should be done with a blade equipped with horizontal teeth so that excessive amounts of top soil will not be removed in the process of uprooting trees and carrying them into windrows or piles. With a root rake and disk, the soil can be prepared for planting at the same time. This way, specific grasses, clovers, or other legumes can be planted to encourage insect life and to provide green forage and seed.

If planting is not intended, good results can usually be attained by encouraging native grasses and other herbaceous plants. In this case, cutting, or spraying with a herbicide will give good results. If the trees are cut with an axe or chainsaw, the stumps should be sprayed to prevent sprouting. Then it will be necessary to basal spray at intervals to keep out undesirable woody vegetation in the future. The common 2, 4-D or 2, 4, 5-T herbicides, or mixtures of the two, in water as a blanket application eliminate the brush but leave the grasses. A much more selective elimination of woody plants can be made by spraying the bottom fourteen inches of each stem with the 2, 4-D—2, 4, 5-T mixture, or 2, 4, 5-T alone, in oil. This can be done with a standard knapsack type sprayer under low pressure.

The entire process of clearing and maintenance can be accomplished with these chemicals. Basal spraying as just described will kill stems up to three or four inches. To kill stems of greater diameter, the bark must be frilled with an axe around the circumference about a foot above the ground and the chemical applied to the open sapwood. Detailed instructions for this operation can be obtained from the chemical companies.

The proper size of these clearings will vary somewhat with local conditions. Where no openings already exist in large timber, they may be as small as one-half acre and fulfill the need. These small openings should be nearly square in out-line rather than long and narrow. Cottontails and other small game species become vulnerable to predation when they get too far from cover and, for that reason, feeding strips should be kept narrow. But turkeys have little to fear in the open. The square or wide clearings permit a maximum of sunshine to reach the earth and insure best production of ground vege-tation and insects. On large natural clearings of several acres, it may be advantageous to plant a strip or two of cereal grains or legumes. Lime and fertilizer usually must be added to insure a good catch and crop of these items. Soil analyses by the county farm agent, or other agency equipped to do such work, are a necessity for best results.

Where should these man-made openings be located? Prob-ably almost any place where the forest occurs in large blocs. This could be on top of a mountain, or along a stream bottom in the valley. There is an advantage in placing them near free water so that older turkeys can secure this necessity close to their source of summer food. Certainly the sites for the openings should be chosen on the basis of soil depth and quality as well. To produce green forage and insect life in abundance, the soil must be productive. Steep slope should be avoided so that soil erosion will not nullify the value of the opening.

In South Carolina and other southern states with extensive pine stands, controlled burning has been used successfully as a wild turkey management tool. By this means, the accumulation of brush, pine straw, and matted grasses are removed, thus opening up the stands of timber and releasing the more desirable herbaceous vegetation. Good grazing is thereby furnished in early spring. Both summer and winter burns can be used with good results, but winter burning is safer. Summer burning should be done only in large timber with extremely dense, heavy stemmed undergrowth, but never where the understory is composed largely of dogwood and other desirable food species, because the kill-back may be severe. Summer burning should not be before August when the turkey nesting season is completed.

The winter burning season is approximately from the first of December, when the vegetation becomes dormant, until late February when the breeding season starts. The cost of this management practice is as low as 15 cents an acre on large tracts.

Controlled burning has also been used as a method of keeping woody growth out of forest clearings. This technique could probably be used with some success almost anywhere, provided precautions were taken not to start a forest fire.

Fire as a management measure is not recommended for mature hardwood stands.

*Natural Food Production.* Normally there is no scarcity of natural foods in the forests at any time of the year if a large part of the timber is mature hardwoods and if the forest is broken by frequent grassy openings. This provides mast foods for fall, winter, and spring, and insects and green forage for late spring, summer and early fall. Of course, a large part of the natural food supply can be cut off by deep snows, and supplemental emergency feeding may be necessary during these times.

If some need is felt to increase the natural food supply for turkeys, it can be done in several ways. As described in a previous section of this chapter, insect and green forage foods can be increased greatly for poult production merely by creating forest openings. When a number of these already occur naturally, the insect production and the quality of the forage can be enhanced by liming and fertilizing and by planting native or introduced grasses and legumes particularly adapted for this purpose. In the East, blue grass (*Poa*) —white clover (*Trifolium repens*) mixtures, orchard grass (*Dactylis glomerata*), certain of the native *Panic* grasses, and others will provide more of the essentials than some of the poorer quality grasses such as broomsedge (*Andropogon virginicus*) or poverty grass (*Aristida dichotoma*).

Foods produced by shrubs, vines, and low-growing trees can be increased greatly oftentimes by release cuttings. Flowering dogwoods, grapevines, greenbriers, persimmons, oaks, cherry, witch hazel, hawthorns, and others in the

North are often suppressed by shade and competition from larger trees of little value to turkeys. If this competing growth is removed so that the sunshine can get to the suppressed plants, they will usually begin to fruit much more heavily. *Release cutting is favored over the planting of food-producing trees, shrubs, and vines because it is much quicker and is usually more effective and economical.*

Fertilization experiments with mast-producing trees (oaks, etc.) to determine the effect of fertilizers on fruit production are underway at the Pennsylvania State University but no conclusive evidence has been obtained as yet. At best, this may be an expensive way to increase food for wild turkeys.

*Food Patch Planting.* It is the writer's opinion that food patch planting of cereal grains and other seed producing plants for wild turkeys is most often an unnecessary and undesirable practice. This is not always true, of course. Of far greater importance is the provision of green forage and insect-producing grasses and legumes for summer food for poults. Clovers and grasses, if heavily grazed or mowed, will continue to provide green forage far into the winter, or over the entire winter, even in the northern states. These are the kinds of food patches which pay greatest dividends.

The same money used to plant a series of grain strips in forest openings or along forest edges would release many hundreds of food producing shrubs and vines which would continue to provide large quantities of food for a great many years. The grains, on the other hand, are usually consumed by early to late fall by all kinds of animals, including the turkeys, and often nothing is left for winter. In good deer country, grain is sometimes not permitted to mature or is quickly stripped soon after the kernels harden.

Food strips of cereals are often booby traps for turkeys. The hunters literally use them as baited areas and consequently may be able to overshoot the birds in that vicinity. Oftentimes game managers and sportsmen are inclined to overrate the value of these patches simply because they see the turkeys using them repeatedly. This does not mean that there is not adequate native food in the forest, nor does it mean that the food patch has contributed to the well-being of the turkeys.

If a decision is made to plant food strips anyway, what should be planted? Field corn is one of the best winter foods, but it should be planted only where it is likely to mature. This excludes many northern, mountainous areas where a short growing season or "frost pockets" make it impossible for the grain to mature. Also, field corn cannot be grown successfully in most places without cultivation at least twice.

Other close relatives of corn are the kaffirs, broom corn, maize, and sorghum. Sorghum was found to be of little value as turkey food in Alabama. Several millets have been tried in various states and produced excellent seed for turkeys. German and red-top millets were good in Alabama, and German, brown top, and proso millets have proved acceptable in South Carolina. Although the millets produce large quantities of seed, song birds may get the bulk of this crop in many places.

In Virginia, soybeans and cowpeas were planted and were taken readily by wild birds. The black soybean contains vitamin A, whereas the yellow does not in any quantity, so that the former is probably preferable. In Pennsylvania buckwheat and duckwheat have been planted extensively for wild turkeys, but in many places the deer will not permit it to grow.

Wheat and rye provide green forage over the winter and ripe grain later in the summer and fall. Oats is another grain which provides both forage and seed. All three of these make valuable nurse crops for sowing grasses, clovers and other legumes.

Chufa *(Cyperus esculentus)*, a sedge which produces underground tubers, is planted all over the South as food for wild turkeys. The tubers are scratched out of the ground and eaten with relish by these birds and also by raccoons, squirrels, and other animals. Sometimes it is desirable to uproot a few of the tubers in the fall so that the birds will discover that they are present. After that, the turkeys will take care of the remainder.

Chufas may be planted as early as April in the deep south and from May 15 to late June in Virginia and other states a little farther north. It is suggested that the land be plowed and harrowed as in the preparation for planting corn, and the seed tubers planted in rows 2½ to 3 feet apart. The tubers should be about 18 inches apart in the row. It takes about a bushel (about 40 pounds) to plant an acre.

If the chufa planting is not entirely consumed, the new growth can be fertilized and disced the following spring, and the second-year patch may be almost as productive as the original one.

Austrian winter peas are used in Alabama as winter turkey food plantings. This legume is an excellent crop for preventing erosion and for enriching the soil.

In South Carolina, fescue and ladino clover pasture appears promising. Technicians there have also planted bahia and bermuda grasses. The bahia are stripped by the turkeys, and both produce good quantities of insects.

There are many other grains, legumes, vines, and shrubs which can be planted for wild turkeys. Each state, and each section of a state, has its own local conditions of climate, soils, animal life, and other factors. These will dictate the food plants which will be most successful and most useful. In all cases, plantings should follow good farming practices. Care should be taken to prevent soil erosion. Liming and fertilization usually is a necessity. As much as five tons of lime to the acre may be necessary to establish legumes on some acid soils. On such soils, other grains or food plants requiring less lime may be more practical. Usually from 200 to 400 pounds of a complete commercial fertilizer is necessary for good growth and yield. Proper soil preparation, cultivation, and, in some cases, weed control is important. Proper site, and proper relationship between the food patch and surrounding cover are imperative.

The best approach for the uninformed and unexperienced person wishing to undertake this kind of management is to seek the advice and assistance of the "experts." The county farm agents, the Soil Conservation Service representatives, land management personnel of the state game department, or the man on the land, the farmer, are all capable and willing to assist the individual sportsman or sportsmen's club in a venture of this kind.

*Spring and Spring Run Improvement.* Food habits studies and observation in the wild have proved that wild turkeys will utilize various foods found in the open spring water in midwinter. Because this food source is often available to turkeys even when other streams are frozen over and when the ground is covered with deep snow, it is believed to be an important feature in the winter survival of these birds in northern states.

Turkeys will glean many kinds of food from these runs and the seepage areas surrounding them. Green forage is one of the most important. Animal foods include various aquatic insect nymphs, salamanders, snails, crayfish, and other miscellaneous animal life. Lush green grass in the adjacent wet areas can be encouraged with liming and fertilization and sometimes seeding. The forage within the water itself can be increased by planting watercress (*Radicula* sp.) or other aquatics. This in turn will provide food and living space for additional animal life. Liming and fertilizing the banks for grass will also aid in starting such aquatics as watercress, because these plant nutrients will gradually leach into the stream itself.

Several of these fine, food-producing spring areas will come close to taking care of the emergency needs of wild turkeys during bad weather, unless the snow and cold are so severe that even this food source is cut off.

## Winter Feeding

The extreme hardiness of the wild turkey has been adequately described under a previous heading *Winter Mortality*. It was shown that birds on experiment lived as long as twenty-four days without food or water, and, during a period of severe snow storms and cold, game farm birds did not leave their roosts for eight days and appeared none the worse for their long fast.

However, under excessively adverse conditions when snow may be more than eighteen inches deep for extended periods, a winter feeding program appears to be desirable, at least from present knowledge of the subject. Artificial feeding over a large area is not the task that it would at first appear to be. This is because these birds have such a large cruising range. Thus, it is possible to have turkeys come to a well located feeder from several miles in any direction, and sometimes two, three, or more flocks can be fed at one central location. Theoretically it is possible for all of the

WIRE BASKET FEEDER

1½" MESH POULTRY WIRE

36"

DIAMETER ANY CONVENIENT SIZE

FASTEN TO TREE WITH BOTTOM 20" ABOVE THE GROUND.

NED SMITH

birds in a twenty-five to forty square mile area to be fed from one feeder. At any rate, a few strategically located feeders will take care of a vast region and the turkeys living in it.

Now how should the job be done? First of all it is advisable to establish permanent feeders. Indiscriminate scattering of feed in many spots over a large area is not recommended. Scratch grain or corn sprinkled over the landscape by hand or from an airplane does not do a good job. Much of the grain becomes unavailable because it is buried beneath the snow, and a large part of it may quickly be eaten by other animals. A large part of the money and effort expended is wasted when feeding is done in this manner. Ear corn stuck on spikes or sharpened sticks is likely to be equally

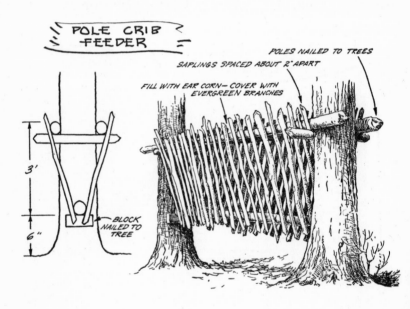

ineffective. In fact, the birds may be frightened by ears of corn presented in this way.

The best system appears to be permanent wire or wooden pole feeders filled with yellow ear corn. Two of these are shown in the accompanying sketch. The pole feeder can be built entirely from material found in the forest. The second is entirely constructed with poles also, except that poultry netting is used to form the top and sides. These feeders will hold several bushels of ear corn and do not need to be filled very often. When roads are impassible for an extended period, this is a real advantage.

Feeders should be located, if possible, where they can be serviced from a truck or jeep. Otherwise, horses or back packs will have to be used to get the feed to the proper place. In mountainous terrain, most birds will spend more time in the sheltered valleys in cold winter weather than they will on higher ground. Therefore, the feeders should be in the small valleys not too far from the streams. Any game manager who studies the winter range of his flocks from their tracks in the snow will soon discover the best feeder locations. And these spots will usually remain good year after year. In flat country, good locations will be determined best through observation of the feeding ranges of the various resident flocks.

Feeding sites should be established under conifers, such as pines or hemlocks, when possible although this is not essential. The trees should be sufficiently large so that the limbs do not cut off vision close to the ground. Turkeys are uncomfortable and in a dangerous position when they cannot see well because of thick brush or low growing limbs.

Now when should these feeders be filled? This may sound like a simple question, but there are a number of complications. There appears to be some advantage in placing a little corn in them before the heavy snowstorms begin so that the turkeys will have the feed located when severe weather does come. This is not so necessary for old established feeders. However, it is obviously undesirable to bait turkeys into feeders during the hunting season, so that this activity should be postponed until after the season closes. Also in bear country, an old bear can make a beautiful mess of kindling out of a well constructed feeder with about two sweeps of his big paw. Then finally, corn costs money and it is expensive to waste much of it for deer, crows, squirrels, and other animals which may not need it particularly. For these reasons, *it is recommended that feeding begin only when an emergency period arises where the feeders are accessible by road.* Where they are not accessible once heavy snows fall, there is little recourse but to fill them in late fall, and refill them whenever possible.

In states where deep snows are likely to come and go periodically, the turkeys will usually ignore the corn entirely when the ground is bare, but return to it immediately when deep snow again covers the ground. This brings up another point. How high should the feeder be from the ground? Normally the bottom is raised approximately twenty inches, and the overall height of the feeder permits the snow to get at least three feet deep before it becomes unservicable. The height of the feeder should be adjusted for the expected maximum snowfall.

In most parts of Pennsylvania and other northeastern states, the feeders can be raised several feet off the ground without impairing their effectiveness. Squirrels frequent these "free meal" sites, and do a splendid job of shelling the corn for the turkeys and other game. The squirrels enter the feeder, remove the corn kernels one at a time, bite out the "eye," and discard the remainder. Thus, there is a constant supply of shelled corn on the ground or snow beneath the feeder. Unfortunately, several squirrels can shell a lot of corn in a few weeks, and this empties the feeders rather rapidly. But for efficient and sure operation of the feeders, these bushytailed rodents seem to be indispensible. The wire mesh or pole slats should be close enough together so that the squirrel can enter but cannot remove the ear of corn. Needless to say, this corn on the ground attracts many deer to the vicinity.

Why corn? There are many reasons why it is the best suited of all grains for this purpose. For one thing it will remain in good condition in these open cribs for weeks, whereas scratch grain and other small grains will often mold. Secondly, it is a highly nutritious food, high in fat for winter warmth, and containing sufficient protein and vitamins to keep the birds in good health over long periods. Yellow corn is high in vitamin A, but white corn is low in this vital substance, so that yellow corn is always preferable. Corn is readily available most places and can be purchased at a reasonable price. Also, it can be kept in large storage cribs back in the forests until time for distribution into the feeders. Other grains cannot be stored so easily nor so cheaply.

# PART III
## HUNTING THE WILD TURKEY

WILD TURKEY hunting is truly an art. This does not mean that all turkey hunters are artists. But it does mean that most of those who bag their bird year after year have developed certain skills which qualify them as masters of the sport. Actually there are relatively few, real honest-to-goodness, turkey hunters in the country. The turkey itself is responsible for this.

The great majority of American sportsmen, in spite of their denials, are basically meat-hunters. For this reason the cottontail rabbit is the most popular game animal. For the least expenditure in time, money, equipment, and effort, it provides the greatest return in the stuff that goes on the table. The deer is the next most popular for much the same reasons. However, the chances of killing one are slimmer, and they are usually more expensive to hunt, so there are fewer deer hunters than rabbit hunters.

Countrywide the wild turkey is not nearly so well distributed as the deer; it is usually scarcer in numbers, and is one of the smartest of all species of game. These three things combine to make it one of the most difficult trophies for the average hunter to acquire. That is why this select group of dyed-in-the-wool turkey hunters is so small.

But at the same time, that is also the reason why the wild turkey is such a remarkable trophy and is so avidly pursued by those who have accepted the challenge presented by this crafty bird. These men have come to the realization that there is much more to modern-day hunting than providing food for himself and his family. In fact, for most the thought of hunting for the table is indeed ridiculous. With the money spent for licenses, equipment, gasoline, meals, board, and a million and one other things the average sportsman could buy ten times as much meat at the butcher shop, and it could be T-bone steaks at that.

These turkey hunters have learned that the real reward of their sport is not meat but healthful, outdoor recreation and the satisfaction of accomplishment. To them it is an opportunity to pit their skills and knowledge against a clever and worthy adversary. The sport becomes a contest of skill, and often of endurance, much like a game of tennis or a boxing match between two contestants. Regardless of the outcome, the real sportsman feels that "the better man won." There are no ill feelings if the hunter goes home empty handed. In fact his respect and admiration for this noble bird is likely to grow as he is outwitted again and again.

And the turkey is most often found in the deep forests where a man has more chance of being alone for a short while—where he can imagine himself a Daniel Boone or a Davy Crockett as he stalks or calls a big gobbler. It takes him away from the unpleasantries of crowded field hunting, dodging shot and wondering how soon he will be evicted by an irate landowner. In the mountains or swamps there is relative peace, a chance to commune with Nature and to absorb its beauties and blessings. A man can return from wild turkey hunting with a feeling of contentment and with the satisfaction of having spent a glorious day afield. Contrast this with the disgruntled rabbit or pheasant hunter who has had too much competition and has perhaps had an unpleasant brush with a landowner.

These are but a few of the more obvious reasons why

turkey hunting is so popular with those who have been properly indoctrinated. Many, many thousands more would become avid followers of the sport if they were only privileged to know its pleasures. With the increase of wild turkeys in so many places, perhaps the ranks of this exclusive brotherhood will increase greatly in the next few years. It is hoped that this book may be the first step of many novices toward mastering the art of turkey seduction.

# Chapter 8:

## Equipment

### Rifle and Shotgun

ANYONE WHO would come right out and flatly state that either the rifle or the shotgun was the better firearm for wild turkey hunting would be sticking his neck out a mile. This argument falls into the same category as the old questions of whether the setter is better than the pointer, or whether natural gut makes a better leader than nylon, or whether a bass puts up a better fight than a trout. Each man has his own ideas based upon experience, usually limited experience. So he will have prejudices one way or another depending upon what has happened to himself and his friends in the past. Or his thinking may be influenced by things he has learned from "old-timers" or from so-called "experts" writing in magazines or books.

The only positive statement that can be made is that they are both excellent wild turkey guns. Either one can be the wrong gun under certain circumstances and exactly the right gun at other times. One thing for sure, however, if a man is carrying his rifle, he will most likely get all flying shots. If he is carrying his shotgun, the turkeys will walk and stand endlessly just nicely out of range. The eager beaver who carries both usually sees nothing and winds up with blisters on both shoulders.

McIlhenny in his book *The Wild Turkey and Its Hunting* states very positively that the rifle is the arm, *par excellence*, for hunting the wild turkey under nearly all conditions. Davis in his book *The American Wild Turkey* says that in his opinion the ideal gun for turkeys is a twelve guage shotgun with thirty inch barrels bored full choke. He backs this up by saying that he believes that a skillful hunter in the course of a season can bag more turkeys with a shotgun than he can with a rifle. This would sound as if two of the best turkey hunters in the country were in complete disagreement. However, this is not entirely true.

It all comes back to the personal interests of the individual hunter. One man prides himself on his shooting ability, and would rather drop a turkey at 150, 200 yards, or more with a scope-sighted rifle than kill a half dozen with a shotgun at close range. So, if you are a marksman and own a "varmint" gun with a six or eight power scope on it, you are more than likely going to carry it for turkeys. The boys who peck away at groundhogs, crows, hawks, prairie dogs, jackrabbits, and all the other "small fry" targets feel awfully foolish shooting a turkey standing at thirty-five yards with a shotgun. In some parts of the country where big game hunting holds the spotlight, many nimrods rarely shoot anything but a rifle. In these areas a large majority of the "natives" will be found carrying their favorite deer rifle, with or without scopes, and in an endless variety of calibers.

Another hunter's greatest satisfaction may lie in outwitting the bird with a turkey caller. To him the shooting is merely incidental to a much more exciting part of the sport. His fun comes from becoming so adept on the caller that he is able to entice even the oldest, wiliest gobblers to him. The appearance of the bird at close range, as the result of his expert calling, is the real reward for him, and the killing of the turkey is actually an anticlimax.

Still a third man is hunting with visions of roast turkey

on his mind, and he is going to use the weapon which he feels is most deadly for the purpose.

It is obvious then that not everyone agrees on either the shotgun or the rifle as the ideal wild turkey gun. Under certain circumstances, one may be favored over the other. But on what basis should the tyro make his choice? What are the desirable features and shortcomings of each?

Let's take the rifle first. In the hands of an excellent shot it can certainly account for a great many turkeys and with few losses. An occasional individual will become good enough to take turkeys with fair regularity even on the wing. Davis tells of a Fleetwood Lanneau who made six successive kills with six shots from a .32-20 repeater as the turkeys flew from a roost one morning in South Carolina. With good sights and a well fitting gun, many marksmen could drop a flying turkey if it were in the open and not too far away. But this is not for the average hunter.

One of the greatest problems in using a rifle successfully on wild turkeys is in getting a good shot. The darned things so often won't hold still and when they do stop it is likely to be behind a tree or some other cover. At close range, a turkey can so easily be spooked when the hunter is trying to line up his sights. A shotgun can be thrown to the shoulder and fired almost instantly. This hardly gives the bird a chance to duck behind a tree or bush. Therefore, it is usually necessary for the hunter to have his rifle shouldered and be prepared to squeeze off the trigger as soon as an open shot is presented. But oftentimes it is almost impossible to get even a half decent snap shot at a weaving, dodging target in thick cover.

A second objection to the rifle is that it so often either

under-kills or over-kills. By that, it is meant that many turkeys are hit and mortally wounded but they are still lost to the hunter. Unless a bird is hit in a vital spot with the slower, non-expanding bullets, the bird is likely to fly or run off to die later. On the other hand, the high speed, mushrooming bullets are likely to make hamburg out of the entire carcass of a big wild turkey. Nothing is more distressing than to pick up a turkey which is about three feet longer than usual because the whole middle has been blown out of it. In states where one is the season limit, this may be doubly distressing. But more about this later.

The third objection to the rifle is that quite often the light may be so poor that it is difficult to find the bird at all in the sights. Sometimes the best opportunities are offered just after daylight or just before dark. Then there are dark, rainy days and even deep shaded woods to add to the difficulties. And there are the usual troubles with wet scope lenses on rainy days. In this kind of weather, it pays to have a quick-detachable mount, because it is impossible to get a crosshair on a bird through a double film of water. Of course, there are ways of overcoming this problem.

And now what about the shotgun? Everything which has been said against the rifle as a turkey gun can be said in favor of the shotgun. It is good for quick shots, for shots in dense cover, for shooting in poor light, and for birds on the wing. In other words it is the ideal weapon at close range, except that it does not present the challenge to the shooter's skill that the rifle does. Other than this, the chief fault of the shotgun is that it definitely has a limited range. If the target is beyond seventy to eighty yards, it is relatively safe even against the most powerful magnums and the heaviest shot.

This does not mean that turkeys are not occasionally killed beyond this range, but certainly it cannot be done with any consistency with any gun or ammunition. In fact, it is exceedingly unsportsmanlike to take these long "prayer shots," because too many of these magnificent birds will be wounded and die later. This would be poor conservation at any time, but particularly so when the species is so relatively scarce over most of its range.

It is obvious then that the rifle's greatest value is its ability to kill turkeys far beyond the effective range of the shotgun and that the shotgun's greatest fault is that it is powerless beyond a certain limited distance. Of course, the rifle is effective at all ranges, but does have certain shortcomings.

This still leaves the beginning hunter up in the air somewhat when it comes to making a choice. My personal recommendation is the shotgun, with the possibility of graduating to the rifle later. But even at that this recommendation is a general one, and would probably be changed for some individuals and for some sections of the country.

One reason I prefer the shotgun is because I like to call turkeys. For that reason a large part of my shooting has been at close range. Secondly, I like to shoot my birds on the wing whenever possible. This is in spite of instructions to the contrary by most authorities. I realize that a bird shot in the head and neck while standing or walking is the surest bet for the average hunter, and it also means less shot in the meat for the table. But I was brought up on wing shooting by a father who would never permit his boys to shoot a bird unless it was on the wing. Although this early training applied only to grouse, ringnecks, quail, and woodcock at the time, it has left an indelible impression on me. In fact, the first several turkeys I killed were all shot on the wing because I considered them an overgrown grouse as far as my hunting ethics were concerned. When a called turkey is in easy shotgun range, I still stand up and take it as it goes away. The flush, and the appearance of this colorful bird in flight, are added delights in my day afield. And I cannot resist giving so noble a bird one more chance to escape.

Some years ago, I was forced to abandon this notion, however. Early in the season in Pennsylvania, two or three inches of soft snow had fallen and I decided to try The Barrens just west of State College in Centre County. I liked to sneak along the back sides of the low ridges crossing the scrub oak flats and occasionally peek over the rim and scan the other side. In this manner, a hunter could locate turkeys from their tracks, or, if lucky, could actually stalk birds. I had hardly gone a half mile when I noticed a bare spot or two in the snow on my side and near the top. Even at a hundred yards or more, I was sure they were turkey scratchings and began to pussyfoot toward them. The top here was very narrow and the sides quite steep so that it was possible to come up one side and look down over the other without showing more than the top of the head. The wet snow killed all noise underfoot.

The scratchings were steaming fresh when I got to them and a few crouched steps put me on top. I carefully raised up and looked over the rim. My first sweep was along the bottom where the timber was rather large and open. Nothing there. I took one more step so that I could scan the sides, and then it happened. Putt! Right under me and not thirty feet away stood a big, old hen. I leveled my shotgun above her and waited for her to flush. And then, not twenty feet to her left, a louder, deeper Putt! There stood a magnificent old gobbler. I immediately swung my gun to him and noticed in a split second that his beard was hanging almost to the snow and his brilliantly pink feet were adorned with long sharp spurs. Here was a real trophy!

I believe yet that these birds could not believe that a human could ever catch them so flatfooted. I swear both birds had a look of complete surprise on their faces and it took them a full three seconds to recover enough to start moving. Both birds started running downhill at a tremendous speed, and I finally decided that they had no intentions of taking wing. At about twenty-five yards I made a bloody pulp out of his head, and that was the first turkey shot on the ground by me. I was honestly disappointed in spite of his size and beauty.

But the beginner should not be influenced too much by my idiocyncracies or sentiments, because turkeys, in spite of their size, have an awfully lot of empty space around them. They can be missed and missed easily.

I should add here that I am also a rifle user and have three scope-sighted rifles at the present time. Nobody gets a greater thrill out of bringing down a turkey, deer, woodchuck, crow, or other game at long range than I do. But I have had so few opportunities on turkeys, where it would be a real test of a rifleman's shooting ability, that I seldom carry one. However, in some of the rugged terrain of northern Pennsylvania, West Virginia, Virginia, and other mountainous states, some extraordinary shots across narrow valleys are sometimes offered. This is particularly true when there is snow on the ground. Some of the more open ranges of the Southwest provide opportunities for long range shooting as well.

## Choosing the Proper Shotgun and Ammunition

The problem of choosing a proper gun and ammunition for wild turkeys is not such a difficult proposition. Because the bird is extra large, extra tough, and likely to be at extra long range, only the most powerful shotguns can be sensibly recommended. I have seen turkeys killed with a .410 gauge, and at close range the twenty-eight, the twenty, or the sixteen are all more than adequate. But at medium to long range they just cannot measure up to the twelve gauge.

In the same way, very fine shot or very heavy shot are likely to cripple and not hold these big birds. One day while grouse hunting, I had a turkey flush off a high bank to my left and fly across in front of me at about forty yards. At both shots, the bird practically stopped in midair, shuddered like a heavy boat hitting a sandbar, and then flew on. Fortunately it flew less than two hundred yards when it was smacked down for keeps by another hunter. I feel sure that the bird was literally loaded with 7½ shot from the two low speed shells I had in my twelve double. A grouse or a quail at the same range would have been killed dead as a doornail by either charge, but not so the big fellows.

I agree heartily with Henry E. Davis in recommending a twelve gauge with thirty inch barrels bored full choke. It matters little whether the gun is a double, a pump, or an automatic. The standard twelve chambered for the 2¾ inch shell, either in the high velocity or magnum load, is entirely adequate for the job. However, the twelve magnum, chambered for the 3 inch shells is unquestionably a real turkey gun, as is the ten magnum. But wild turkey hunting usually involves a certain amount of walking, and these big magnums can get mighty heavy after a few miles or a few hours. If a man is going to sit and wait, or do a lot of calling and not too much walking, these heavyweights can be tolerated. But never, never shoot your bird in the body at close range with one of these, unless you want it to look like a sieve.

The sixteen gauge and the twenty magnum are reasonably satisfactory for turkeys, but the user should recognize their limitations. He should not try to kill these birds beyond forty to fifty yards with shot of any size.

Speaking of light gauges for turkeys reminds me of an experience a few years ago. A very good friend and hunting companion had a son, Rick, who had reached his fourteenth birthday. He had bought the boy a .410 double and during the summer had taught him how to handle the gun safely and how to shoot. The only shooting experience the lad had prior to the opening of the hunting season was on a few stationary tin cans and some hand-thrown clay targets.

On the first day of the wild turkey season, four of us including Rick drove north into the heart of the Pennsylvania turkey country. Because of the long drive, we arrived later than we had anticipated, and the hunters had already been in the woods an hour or more. Naturally some flocks had been scattered. Within a half mile of where we intended to park, we rounded a curve in the mountain dirt road and a turkey ran across just below us. It scaled a steep fifteen-foot bank on the left side of the road and disappeared into an old clearing. I quickly stopped the car out of sight behind the bank. On instruction, Rick jumped out, loaded his gun, and we climbed the bank together. We cautiously peeked over the top and there stood the turkey not twenty yards away. He raised his gun, took very deliberate aim at the head and neck, and killed a nice hen turkey the first time he had ever fired a gun at game of any kind!

In selecting a shotgun, it will pay the buyer to pattern the weapon. Some full choked guns will not shoot a good tight pattern with the size shot recommended for turkeys. The ideal gun should put 75% or better of high velocity 6's, 5's, or 4's into a 30 inch circle at 40 yards. With this kind of performance, few turkeys are going to run or fly away when covered with the pattern.

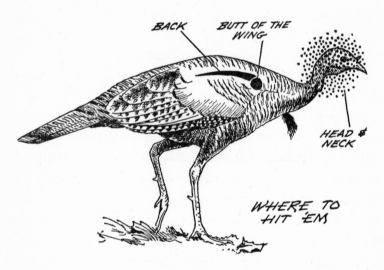

Some hints have already been given about shot size and kind of ammunition. Nothing but high velocity or magnum loads should be used. (Don't try to shoot a 3 inch magnum shell in a gun with 2¾ inch chambers unless your insurance is paid up.) Recommended shot sizes are 6's, 5's, and 4's. High speed 7½'s are deadly at ranges up to about 35 to 40 yards when aimed at the head and neck and are preferred by many old timers who call their turkeys up close. But 7½'s in the body at forty to fifty yards may merely make the bird run or fly faster and perhaps die later. Sixes are good for head and neck shots and are sufficiently heavy to knock down a flying bird at decent range. Fives or 4's are best for body shots. The new 2¾ inch magnum shell in 4's is a very fine load for long range shooting either in the air or on the ground. Three inch magnum loads in both 4's and 2's are good.

BB's or buckshot of any size are not recommended under any circumstances. The pattern at long ranges is so poor that many more birds will be mortally wounded and escape than will be killed outright. This kind of shooting is unsportsmanlike and is exceedingly poor conservation.

When I first started wild turkey hunting, I followed the recommendations for shot size on the charts put out by ammunition companies. These were obviously made up by someone who had never hunted turkeys because 2's and BB's were suggested. At any rate, my first turkey was killed at about seventy-five to eighty yards with a load of 2's in the left barrel of a twelve double. I walked into a flock on the rim of a mountain and had about fifteen birds flush from the ground and trees like a covey of giant quail. A gobbler hesitated a little longer than the rest, soared out of the top of an oak tree and headed out over the valley. I pulled in front of him about twelve feet or so, and at the crack of the gun he folded as pretty as could be. He lit away down over the steep side and kicked and somersaulted another fifty yards or more before he came to a stop. This bird had been hit by exactly one shot, and do you know where? It went completely through the head about an inch above and behind the eye. That was one of those shots which could never happen to me again in a hundred years.

Buckshot are almost worthless for turkey hunting. Beyond forty yards they scatter so badly that there is little chance of hitting one. And at long ranges, a single buckshot through a non-vital spot is unlikely to hold a bird. This means a cripple, probably lost to the shooter and to all hunters of the region. Davis tells of a hunter who crawled up to within one hundred and twenty-five yards of a flock of turkeys and fired a load of buckshot toward the spot where the birds were thickest. None of these were touched, but a solitary hen feeding fully twenty-five yards to one side was killed instantly. The hunter was unable to say whether she had been killed by a wild shot or by a richochet from a tree or stump.

Those who defend buckshot for turkeys and geese do not realize that the killing power of a shotgun is measured according to the density of its pattern. Experiments have shown that 3 to 5 hits with pellets of a size to give adequate penetration are required for a clean kill. This means that an ordinary full-choked 12 gauge gun is unlikely to put 3 to 5 pellets of No. 2's or larger in a bird the size of a wild turkey beyond 60 yards. With buckshot, there really is no such thing as a pattern in the true sense. Even with No. 4 buck, the smallest size made (27 pellets in 1¼ oz. load), the very best barrel could not be expected to put more than 5 in a 30 inch circle at 80 yards. And at 100 yards or more, it is a lucky shot when the target is touched at all. And often the full choked barrel scatters these large pellets more than barrels with less choke.

Because the No. 1 buck loads only 16 to the 1¼ ounce load, the No. 0 only 12 and the No. 00 only 9, it is obvious that the chance of hitting a turkey at long range with these is certainly remote. But these same "bigshot" hunters will say, "But man, you only have to hit a bird with one pellet and he's yours." This is not true. At longer ranges, a buckshot must hit an extremely vital spot to register a clean, quick kill. Otherwise a bird can often carry them for miles before dying. Thus there are two uncertainties: hitting the bird with the sparse pattern and hitting in a vital spot.

Before we leave the subject of shotguns for wild turkeys, the shotgun-rifle combination should be considered. The light, foreign-made over-and-unders or three-barrel guns are perhaps just about the ideal weapon for the man who really wants to bring home the bacon. Naturally, the double shotgun with the rifle barrel below is better, because two shots are mighty handy at times. But the over-and-under shotgun-rifle combination is fine, too. So many of the "liberated" German guns of this type are twelve and sixteen gauge with heavy deer or bear calibers underneath. These can be relined and remodeled to shoot smaller cartridges of American make but at considerable cost. But some are already 7 mm. or smaller and can be used successfully with handloads without any changes. Still others are made for standard American cartridges.

The ideal combination would be a twelve double, full choke, with the rifle barrel chambered for the .22 Hornet or some other small bore cartridge. This gun could be equipped with open sights or with a quick-detachable scope of four or six power. Most of the German guns are equipped with permanent scope mounts of this kind.

*Choosing the Proper Rifle, Ammunition and Sights*

The man who decides to use a rifle for turkey hunting has an infinitely great choice of types and calibers. Any caliber rifle will kill a turkey if the bird is hit in the right place. But some definitely have too little punch to be dependable, while others pack so much wallop that the meat you intended to eat is scattered all over a quarter-acre. Cartridges with low velocities are likely to be of little value for long range shooting. Some calibers are just naturally too big for turkeys.

When all of the objections are satisfied, perhaps there aren't so many good turkey cartridges after all. The common .22 Short, Long, Long Rifle, W.R.F., and the .25 rimfire are not recommended because they are not powerful enough to anchor a mature wild turkey unless hit in a very vital spot. Naturally a head, neck, or backbone shot would be effective even with these small loads. And perhaps death would be rapid enough or the shock great enough, if the bullet passed through the heart or liver, to keep the bird from running or flying away. But if hit almost anywhere else, through the breast or intestinal region, the hunter is probably going to be looking for his bird a long way off.

At the opposite extreme are such calibers as the .300 and .375 Magnums, the .358 Winchester, the .35 Remington, the .348 Winchester, and the .405 Winchester. These are designed for moose, grizzlies, elk, and other of the largest North American big game animals. To shoot a turkey with one of these would be like shooting a chipmunk with a .30-.30.

Between these two extremes come a great variety of possible turkey cartridges. There are the "varmint" rifles, including several standard factory models and the various wildcats put out by the custom builders. The factory cartridges include such well-known calibers as .22 Hornet, .218 Bee, .219 Zipper, .222 Remington, .220 Swift, and .22 Savage. The .243 Winchester and the .244 Remington should also be included in this list although they can be classed as good "deer" cartridges as well. No attempt is going to be made to name the wildcats because there are dozens of them, mostly created by modifying standard cases. Generally speaking, the wildcats are too fast and have too much "splatter" to use with expanding bullets. If these cartridges are to be used for body shooting turkeys, a full jacketed bullet will almost have to be used to prevent total destruction of the meat. These same restrictions hold true for the .220 Swift, the .219 Zipper, the .243 Winchester, the .244 Remington, and the .22 Savage because they are also ultrafast and terrifically destructive to flesh. Of course, if the rifleman has sufficient self-confidence to shoot at head or neck only, any type bullet is satisfactory.

The .22 Hornet, the .218 Bee, and the .222 Remington are perhaps the best of the varmint size cartridges for wild turkeys. Standard factory ammunition or handloads with expanding bullets should be used, but care should be taken not to shoot the birds through the breast or guts. The .25-20 and the .25-35 cannot be highly recommended for turkeys. In the hands of a good rifleman they are quite effective, but do not have sufficient shocking power for the average hunter's use.

The other group of calibers which can be used reasonably satisfactorily are the ones commonly used for deer. This includes the .250 Savage, the .257 Roberts, the .270, the

7 mm., the .30-30, the .308 Winchester, the .30-06, the .30-40 Krag and other similar calibers and the various wild-cats built in this size range. These, too, should be hand-loaded with non-expanding bullets for body shooting.

No specific detail is going to be given for handloading different loads for turkeys. Nearly any good custom loader should be able to provide the reader with a good combina-tion of accuracy, shocking power, and limited expansion if he is told what is needed or desired. The books and manuals on handloading will furnish the amateur with a lot of usable information if he wants to experiment. Woodchucks, and other small pest animals, furnish good targets for testing different handloads for turkeys. Any bullet that will anchor an old groundhog at fairly long range without destroying too much flesh should be satisfactory for turkeys.

A couple of general hints might be in order. If expanding bullets are used, flesh destruction (and also shocking power) can be reduced by lowering the velocity. This can be accom-plished by reducing the powder charge or by using a heavier bullet. On the other hand, if a non-expanding bullet is used, the shocking power can be increased by raising the velocity or by reducing the weight of the bullet. Also, by using vari-ous types of expanding bullets, such as soft points, hollow points, etc., the amount of shocking power and flesh de-struction can be altered greatly. With these variables to play with, the handloader should be able to come up with a load which just about fills the bill for his particular rifle and for his kind of hunting.

And now, what about sights? Davis states flatly that the telescope sight is a *must* on a modern hunting rifle. This certainly applies to the turkey gun. Again, this does not mean that iron sights are not effective at close range and, in the hands of an expert, reasonably so at long range. The story is told that Davy Crockett, when a boy, was given one ball and one charge of powder by his father each morning. If he returned with no game, he had no dinner. No wonder Davy and other backwoods boys learned to shoot so well. It was either that or starvation!

Certainly Daniel Boone and the other early pioneers killed thousands of these birds with comparatively crude iron sights. Of course, there are few records to indicate the crippling loss in those days, either.

If iron sights are used, a good hunting peep sight is recommended. Target peep apertures are excellent in good light but of little value on dark days or in deep shade against an almost black target.

The ideal scope for wild turkey hunting should be light in weight, should have a wide field of view, excellent light-gathering properties and preferably with coated lenses, good resolving power, reasonably high magnification, and either cross-hair or dot reticule.

The long target scopes are not recommended for the turkey rifle simply because they are unnecessarily heavy and clumsy for carrying in the woods. Also, most of them are of much higher magnification than needed.

Most modern hunting scopes do provide a wide field of view and have excellent light-gathering qualities. Most have coated lenses, also. Without these attributes, they would sell very poorly and would be forced off the market rather quickly. The cheap scopes manufactured for standard .22 caliber rifles fulfill few of the specifications of a good turkey hunting scope and should not be considered for the purpose.

Low-power scopes, such as the 2½x and 3x, hardly have sufficient magnification for turkey hunting. They are excellent for big game, and especially so if the deer or other animal is running. But this low power is a handicap if the bird is sitting in the top of a thick pine or on the ground in dense cover. Only the higher power scopes will have sufficient resolving power to pick out a bird in thick cover or poor light. Therefore, probably the 4x, 5x, or 6x may be about right, with possibly as much as an 8x for ultra long range shooting. Some of the variable powered scopes make an excellent deer-turkey combination on the same rifle.

Davis and others have experimented a lot with different type reticules, but the fine crosshair or the suspended dot types appear to be best by far. The post, and combination post-crosshair types, are not recommended. My own preference is toward the tackhole dot, but crosshairs are just as deadly.

In rainy weather, waterproof lens covers of some type should be used to keep them free of water. Nothing is more discouraging than to have an opportunity at a big gobbler and then discover that you can't see through your scope. A few soft facial tissues should be carried to wipe off any water which may get on the surface of the lenses. Needless to say, the sealed "all-weather" scopes are best in this kind of weather because the non-sealed type will fog up inside. However, most modern scopes are weatherproofed.

Before leaving the subject of rifles for turkeys, I should like to recount a few experiences which occurred during two successive hunting seasons in Pennsylvania. These illustrate that a turkey must be hit right, with almost any rifle, to kill it instantly and that a turkey hunter should do his darndest to hit them in the proper place.

During the 1952 season, I was hunting in the high mountain country (high for Pennsylvania) in Cameron County. Our small party had split up and each had taken off in a different direction. A couple of inches of soft snow covered the ground and tracking conditions were ideal.

I climbed a ridge just west of the car and had just crossed the top when I hit a fresh single track heading back along the top of the ridge. The north side of this ridge was pretty well blanketed with thick laurel. I knew from past experience that with luck and quiet stalking it was often possible to flush birds out of this thick cover close enough to kill them with a shotgun. So, I decided to follow the tracks.

Within a quarter of a mile, I skirted a particularly thick clump of laurel and found no tracks when I reached the opposite side. I began to circle and found them cutting out at a sharp right angle and going downhill on the dead run. And here and there among the tracks was a drop or two of blood. I backtracked to the middle of the laurel clump and found where the bird had been hiding. Here was a good-sized pool of blood.

Knowing that the bird was injured, I took after him at a fast walk. He circled and zig-zagged through the laurel for a full half-mile and finally broke out into the big timber toward the bottom of the ridge. He crossed this open timber and the stream bottom with tremendous strides, showing that he was travelling at top speed. The opposite slope facing the sun was covered with big timber also and was exceedingly bare of ground cover. But I could see no movement anywhere on the blanket of white snow. I decided that the bird had already crossed the top and out of sight, but the thought of retrieving this crippled bird and preventing its waste intrigued me. The steep slope ahead looked a good mile to the top, but I began my slipping sliding ascent anyway.

As I climbed, I paid little attention to anything except my footing and to keep in general line with the tracks. But about one-third of the way to the top, a sudden movement caught my eye, and there was my turkey heading up the hill for all he was worth. He had stopped and crouched in a depression left when a tree had uprooted many years before. When I first noticed him he was fully 65 to 70 yards away. I could see he was sick and not running like a healthy bird, but I was certainly not about to set any hundred yard dash records running up a 60 degree slope covered with snow. So, I began to shoot, hopefully. I kept shooting and running and finally used up nine shells and all of the oxygen in the valley before a lucky pellet stopped him. My partners told me later that they thought a small war had broken out in that particular valley.

When I examined the bird, I found that a rifle bullet had taken him right across the front of his breast, broken both wings at the elbows, completely shot the crop away and the entire point of the breast. A piece of white meat fully as big as a baseball had been blown away with the crop. And he still wasn't ready to give up!

Just by luck we found out the rest of the story. One of my hunting companions met a man hunting with a .30-30 Winchester with open sights fully a mile and a half from where I finally stopped the bird. He said that he had hit a gobbler, knocked him head over heels, and then watched him get up and run off. He followed the tracks for about a quarter of a mile until the bird went under the wire into a game refuge. Apparently it went straight across and out the other side, because I picked up the track perhaps a quarter mile or a little more straight beyond the upper refuge line.

The hunting season of 1953 provided even more lessons in rifle shooting. One of my co-workers used a .22 Hornet with factory ammunition for his turkey hunting that year. Over a two-day period he had three opportunities to kill turkeys at good range and had all of them get up and leave. The first two birds were knocked flat, flopped and fluttered around, but were gone before the shooter could get to them. He was convinced that the first gathered itself up and flew away, but believes the second ran off. Of course he will never know for sure, but he is satisfied that he must have hit both in the meaty part of the breast.

The third was an unusual experience. Just before five o'clock, the legal closing hour in Pennsylvania, he shot a gobbler with the Hornet. The bird reacted much like the other two. It went down, finally recovered, and flew completely across the valley and lit on the opposite side. Because it was nearly dark, he decided not to attempt to find the bird that night. Early the next morning he was on the spot just after daylight. With a little search, he found where the bird had landed in the snow. In a previous chapter (*Adult Predation*) an account was given of how this badly crippled bird had fought off a fox during the night even though it was attacked several times.

At daylight or soon after, this turkey began to move. The hunter took the tracks in the snow. It travelled to the end of the ridge, off the face, across the valley, up the long steep mountain on the other side, and finally was jumped out of some thick laurel on the back slope fully two hours later.

This time it was brought crashing to earth with a charge from a twelve gauge shotgun. This was another bird with a large part of its breast shot away and still able to fly!

That same season another friend was hunting bears with his .30-06 with ordinary expanding bullets in McKean County, Pennsylvania. The wild turkey season was in at the same time and, like many Pennsylvania bear hunters, he was looking harder for turkeys than he was for bears. About mid-morning, he spotted a flock of birds just under the rim of one of the high ridges. He picked out one of the largest gobblers, held for the middle with his open sights, and touched it off. The bird flattened, flopped and kicked, and then got up and flew with the others. This bird flew across the upper end of a natural basin and lit on the opposite mountainside.

Just as this friend reached the other side to hunt for his bird, he ran into me. Together we searched a good-sized area but could not find where it had landed in the snow. Finally, we decided to separate, and each hunt in a different direction for his cripple. I had hardly walked a hunderd yards when a very large gobbler flushed only a short distance ahead. He appeared to fly perfectly normally and went out of sight around a curve in the mountain.

When I reached the spot from which the gobbler had flushed, I found blood in his tracks. I backtrailed a little and found where he had dropped in the snow. There the snow was stained crimson in a circle a foot or more in diameter, and hanging on a laurel bush nearby was at least a foot and a half of his intestines. A little farther along his trail was another large piece and more blood.

From this I knew that the bird was mortally wounded. I

took his line of flight as nearly as I could and worked my way out the side of the mountain. About three hundred yards away I walked directly onto a nineteen pound gobbler with a beautiful long beard lying flat on his back and stone dead. Evidently this bird had died or at least collapsed in mid-air.

The bullet had opened up the body cavity and removed the rear tip of the breast. Practically all of its intestines were gone.

These incidents, and many more like them, clearly prove that the wild turkey is a tough bird and takes a lot of killing. It also proves that the important thing in using a rifle is to hit them in the right place. And the right place is not in the breast! The accompanying illustration shows where a turkey should be shot with a rifle, both to keep them solidly anchored and to keep from ruining a lot of meat.

The place to hold, if you are not shooting for the head or neck, is for the butt of the wing where it attaches to the body. The idea is to get above the breast meat and through the rib area or backbone surrounding the lungs and heart. Of course, any place where the backbone is shattered, from its juncture with the neck to within a couple of inches of the tail, the results will be highly satisfactory. This means that the shooter should hold high and try to catch the bird in the top three inches of its body and as far front as possible. A gut shot is unpleasant at best, especially with an expanding bullet, and may cause the meat to be wasted unless the bird is dressed and thoroughly washed very quickly. The odor and taste will permeate the meat quite rapidly even in cool weather.

## Turkey Callers

Obviously a gun and some ammunition to go with it are the only really essential items for hunting the wild turkey unless a man wants to try them with the bow and arrow. Taking a truly wild turkey in this manner would surely be one of the most difficult feats in all sportsdom. The cards would all be stacked against the archer.

Regardless of what kind of weapon is used, the turkey caller is probably the next most important item of equipment. There are two reasons why the caller should be a *must* for the real turkey hunter (but not for the hunter who does not know how to use them.) First of all, it so often contributes so much to the success of the hunt. The man who relies solely upon his stalking ability or upon dumb luck is much less likely to "bring home the bacon." The second reason is that it adds so much to the real sport and enjoyment of turkey hunting. The expert on the turkey caller is much like the dry fly fisherman.

Dry fly fishing for trout is so popular because it presents a challenge above and beyond just hooking and landing fish. The right fly must be selected for the particular water and time of year, it must be cast skillfully to exactly the right place and must light on the water as light as thistledown. It must then float high and dry without any line drag, and be picked up again without disturbing the surface of the water. When a fish strikes, the hook must be set immediately but so very lightly to prevent snapping the thread-like tippet. And finally, the fish must be played artfully so that the tiny hook will not pull out or break away. How different from the average worm fisherman who plunks his bait into

# COMMERCIAL CALLERS

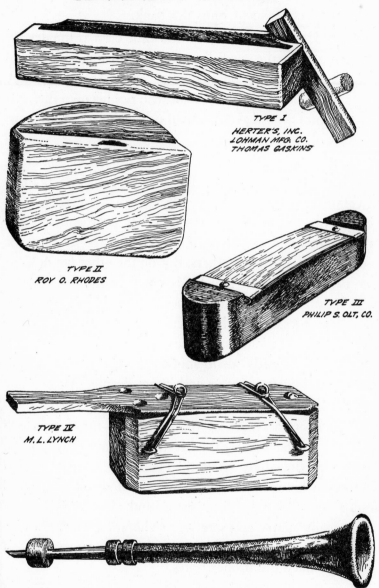

TYPE I
HERTER'S, INC.
LOHMAN MFG. CO.
THOMAS GASKINS

TYPE II
ROY O. RHODES

TYPE III
PHILIP S. OLT, CO.

TYPE IV
M. L. LYNCH

TYPE VII - TOM TURPIN

the middle of a pool, feels the bite, waits a moment, and then swings his fish out onto the bank.

The expert turkey caller is in the same class as the dry fly fisherman. He is the specialist who gets so much more out of his outdoor recreation than the "chase 'em up" turkey hunter. And like the fly fisherman who ties his own flies, the turkey hunter who makes his own calls can extend his sport into the dull winter months.

The most common question asked by the beginner is, what kind of caller is best? There is probably no positive answer to this question. Generally it can be answered by saying, "the one which works best." It is true that more turkey sounds and more natural-sounding notes can be made on certain types than on others. But on the other hand, some hunters can operate certain kinds much better than others. As an example, some of the types which are placed in the mouth may be exceedingly difficult for some to use because of differences in mouth construction. One man's teeth will be spaced differently than another's, or the roof of his mouth may be narrower or arch more deeply. All of these things will affect the sounds produced.

There are two classes of turkey callers—those in which the sound is produced by the breath and those in which the sound is produced by friction. There are literally dozens of different kinds of callers. Many are of the same general pattern but differ in size, shape and design. Some are mechanically simple and some are elaborate. Some are easily operated and others require a great amount of practice and skill to produce the proper notes.

Before describing the various breath-operated and friction callers, it might be well to say that the most perfect imitations of the wild turkeys language are made by the human voice without any mechanical aid whatsoever. Very few fortunate individuals are so gifted or so trained, but throughout the country there can be found the occasional hunter who has mastered the art. The early Indians were said to be good at these vocal imitations, but their ability came from years of constant practice. After all, their living partly depended upon being able to call the various food animals to within range of their bows or spears. Even today, the Indians and Eskimos in northern North America are noted for their adeptness at calling many game birds and mammals with their voices.

The usual method of imitating the turkey with the human voice is to produce the sounds deep in the throat as the breath is expelled. The depth, tone, and pitch is governed by opening or closing the mouth and by cupping the hands over the mouth. By moving the lower jaw and the Adam's apple up and down, the jerkiness or tremor of the natural note can be reproduced as well. One of my acquaintances, Leo Graham, from Altoona, Pennsylvania, who is a pastmaster at this business, calls by inhaling instead of exhaling. He can imitate all the different yelps and can even gobble very satisfactorily. When yelping, his head, mouth, and neck perform much the same antics as those of the bird itself when making the same notes. No wonder his calling sounds so natural!

I would recommend that every serious turkey hunter at least try his voice and see if it might be suited for calling. There is a lot of real satisfaction for anyone who can master this art. Just think, you would never forget your caller, it

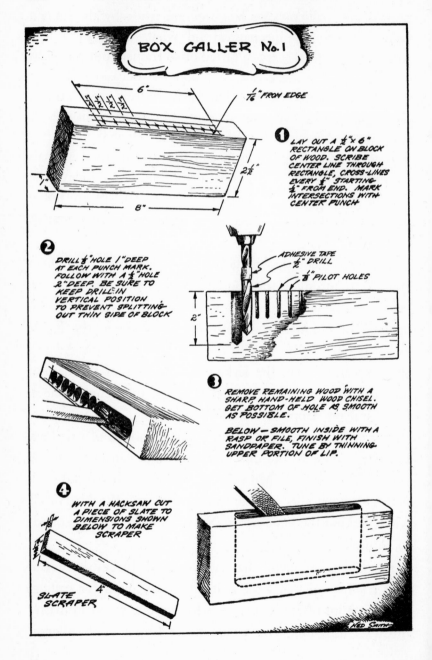

BOX CALLER No. 1

① LAY OUT A ½"× 6" RECTANGLE ON BLOCK OF WOOD. SCRIBE CENTER LINE THROUGH RECTANGLE, CROSS-LINES EVERY ½" STARTING ½" FROM END. MARK INTERSECTIONS WITH CENTER PUNCH

½" FROM EDGE

② DRILL ⅛"HOLE 1"DEEP AT EACH PUNCH MARK. FOLLOW WITH A ½"HOLE 2"DEEP. BE SURE TO KEEP DRILL IN VERTICAL POSITION TO PREVENT SPLITTING OUT THIN SIDE OF BLOCK

ADHESIVE TAPE
½" DRILL
⅛" PILOT HOLES

③ REMOVE REMAINING WOOD WITH A SHARP HAND-HELD WOOD CHISEL. GET BOTTOM OF HOLE AS SMOOTH AS POSSIBLE.

BELOW — SMOOTH INSIDE WITH A RASP OR FILE, FINISH WITH SANDPAPER. TUNE BY THINNING UPPER PORTION OF LIP.

④ WITH A HACKSAW CUT A PIECE OF SLATE TO DIMENSIONS SHOWN BELOW TO MAKE SCRAPER

SLATE SCRAPER

NED SMITH

couldn't get lost or broken or wet, and it would be so convenient to carry. Of course, you could catch a cold!

*Friction-type callers.* If all of the friction-type callers and
their variations were described, it would require a volume
in itself. Only the most common types will be considered
here.

The friction-type callers are not nearly so versatile as the
breath-operated callers. They are almost exclusively used
for imitating the yelp of the turkey. The expert can cluck,
but at best this is risky business because of its similarity to
the alarm "pert."

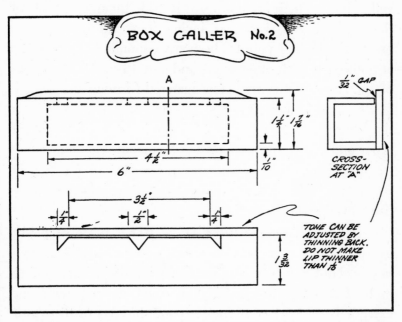

*Common box callers.* This is the type with ten thousand
models. I know of four which are made commercially. One
popular commercial model is long and narrow and square
across the end. The standard one is about 6 inches long,

1 inch high and 1 inch wide. Along one side the lip is raised about ⅛ of in inch to form a sounding board. One end is drilled and the scraper and chalk are carried inside the hollow box and held inside with a cork. This caller is most often made of red cedar. The scraper is made of the same material and is approximately 3 inches long by 1½ inch square, and is solid. This caller is produced commercially by at least three companies. This is pictured as type I in the drawings.

A second commercial type (see type II) is about 3½ inches long, about 2½ inches high, about 11/16 inches thick, and hollow. The sounding board is made by an extension of the flat back and rises 9/16 inches above the body of the box at the highest point. The convex sounding board starts at nothing at both outer edges and rises to the highest point of the arc in the center. The material forming the back is ⅛ of an inch thick. The box is made of poplar except for the back which is red cedar. The scraper is also made of cedar and is 3¼ inches long by ⅞ inches wide and about ¼ of an inch thick at the center. The face of the scraper is rounded. This caller is manufactured by only one company to my knowledge.

Another commercial caller (type III) is made of plastic except for the "lid" which acts as a sounding board. This one is about 4 inches long ⅞ of an inch wide, and 1 inch high. The red cedar top is 1 1/16 of an inch wide and extends about 3/32 of an inch beyond the edge of the plastic box on both sides. This one will yelp on either edge and is customarily operated by scraping on a chalked portion of the gun stock. A wooden or slate scraper of the proper size can be substituted. This one is made by one company only.

The fourth and last commercially made box caller (at least to my knowledge) is the one known as the Gibson caller (type IV). This is perhaps the most famous box caller of the lot and is said to have originated in Missouri. It is a large call being about 11 inches in length overall. In the next chapter, the reader is going to be told how to make this caller at home, so no detailed measurements will be given here. Red cedar is no good for this one and most are made of poplar. Henry Davis made a good one of seasoned holly fitted with an ebony cover. Probably other hard, close-grained woods would also work. Some hunters object to the Gibson because it is large and more difficult to carry than the smaller callers. Also, unless you put a rubber band under the lid, it will yelp as you walk (but not very accurately) and perhaps frighten turkeys in the vicinity.

The final type of box caller (type V) which will be described is about 6 inches long, 1¼ inches wide, and 1 3/32 of an inch high. This hollow box is also usually made of cedar. The lid of the same material is made very thin, about 1/10 of an inch thick. The lip of the lid projects over the edge of the box about 3/16 of an inch and the side immediately underneath is notched out somewhat. The scraper is a piece of slate about 4 x 1 3/16 x ⅛. Directions are given for making this caller in the next chapter, also.

*Other friction type callers.* In southern Pennsylvania and into northern Maryland, a cocoanut shell caller is popular. Just how widespread is its use and popularity, I do not know. The amplifier in this case is the cupped end of a small cocoanut shell. The shell is scraped and rasped until the fibrous material has all been removed and the shell itself

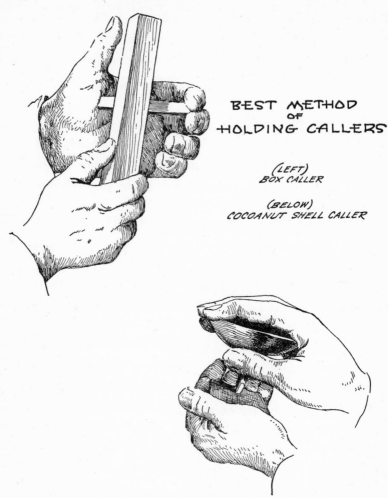

BEST METHOD
OF
HOLDING CALLERS

*(LEFT)*
*BOX CALLER*

*(BELOW)*
*COCOANUT SHELL CALLER*

is quite thin. Then a hole is bored through the center and a laurel peg inserted. The sharpened tip of the peg is scraped over a square piece of thin slate to produce the yelp of the wild turkey. Instructions will be given for constructing this call.

Another is made with a piece of corn cob with a headless nail driven into it. The head of the nail is then scraped over a piece of slate. Still another of the same type is made from a gourd or cowhorn with a piece of yellow pine (fat pine) like a cork pressed into the neck. The end of the stopper is tapered and rounded, and kept heavily coated with chalk or rosin. This tip is rubbed over a flat piece of slate to produce the yelp.

As stated before, there are a million and one different "Rube Goldbergs" of this type. These represent the products of the imaginations of turkey hunters all over the country. Most are no good, but a few have exceptional quality and indicate real ingenuity on the part of the maker. Probably many turkey hunters who read this book will want to experiment a little as well.

There are a few hints which will be helpful to the hunter in getting best results from his box callers. They should be kept dry for one thing. If the edge of the sounding board gets a drop or two of rain on it or a little snow, the resulting squeaks and squawks will frighten every turkey out of the country. Also, just plain dampness will change the tone of the box. The caller should be wrapped in a dark piece of woolen cloth or in a sheet of waterproof plastic. This wrapping will often prevent breakage as well.

The caller should be carried in a pocket where it is least likely to get smashed if the hunter falls or bumps into a tree. Probably a front pocket is best.

As the box caller is carried or used, the edge of the sounding board and the working surface of the scraper become smooth and shiny, and it is difficult to get a good yelp from it. In fact, two polished surfaces of this kind are more likely to produce high squawking notes. To overcome this problem, two additional pieces of equipment are necessary. One is a piece or two of fine sandpaper (No. ½) and the other is a supply of soft chalk. Powdered rosin can be substituted for chalk but is more difficult to carry and use.

Perhaps once or twice during a day's hunt, if the caller is used several different times, it will be necessary to sand the edge of the sounding board and the upper face of the wooden or slate scraper. Be careful not to sand too hard nor too long, particularly on the sounding board, because you could sand it completely away in no time. When the extension of the lip of the sounding board is reduced by sanding, the caller will make higher and higher notes. Just give it two or three light sweeps to scratch off the polished appearance. Then chalk both the edges of the sounding board and the surface of scraper (slate or wood). The chalk should be the very soft kind, similar to carpenter's chalk, and should not be the kind normally used for blackboard work in school. For the cocoanut shell caller, sandpaper alone is used, and both the tip of the laurel peg and the slate is sanded lightly almost every time it is used.

*Breath-Operated Callers.* Probably the simplest of all callers in this class are various kinds of green leaves, and they are considered by many old hunters to be the best of the lot. They are used most extensively in the South, where green leaves are more likely to be available during the hunting season. The leaves of yellow jessamine and of the swamp china briar are considered best in the southern states. With these leaves almost any call of the turkey, except the gobble, can be reproduced.

The leaf is grasped at each end by the thumb and forefinger of each hand. It is then held taut between the front part of the nearly closed lips, and the sounds are produced by blowing against the edge of the leaf. Some hunters call with a leaf by inhaling instead of exhaling. Still others use the leaf of the wild swamp violet by placing it in the back of the mouth. The leaves are kept fresh and handy by carrying them immersed in water in a small water-tight jar. Like so many other things, the use of a natural leaf is probably old fashioned and unnecessarily bothersome. With the great assortment and diversity of rubber and plastic sheeting of all kinds, it only requires a little experimenting to find a completely satisfactory substitute for the leaf. These should be cut in strips about ¾ of an inch wide.

A second simple caller of this type (VI) is made from a piece of metal and a thin strip of rubber. This one is referred to as a diaphragm caller in the text. In the next chapter, directions are given for making it.

This one is placed on the tongue with the free edge of the rubber toward the lips. Then it is pushed backward and upward to the roof of the mouth. Then by short puffs and pants originating back in the throat, the yelps, squeals, clucks, and kees are made. This is one of the most natural sounding callers of all and is very easy to make and carry. However, some hunters have difficulty in locating the right spot in their mouths, and may not be able to produce any sound at all at first.

I have known a number of Pennsylvania hunters who could use this caller to perfection. If you turned your back and walked a little distance away, you would be willing to bet that the real McCoy was standing behind you. By opening and closing the lips and changing the shape of the mouth, almost any tone can be produced. This makes it ideal for the different yelps and the lost call of the young bird. I certainly recommend this caller highly.

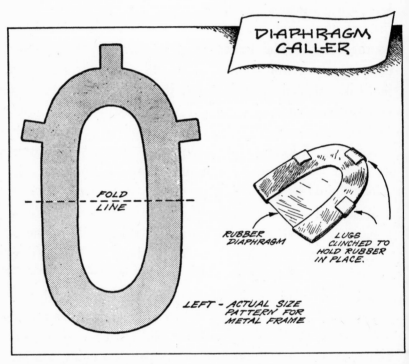

DIAPHRAGM CALLER

FOLD LINE

RUBBER DIAPHRAGM

LUGS CLINCHED TO HOLD RUBBER IN PLACE.

LEFT - ACTUAL SIZE PATTERN FOR METAL FRAME

A third type (VII), and probably the one most used country-wide, is the wingbone caller in its various modifications. This is the smaller of the two bones found in the second joint of the wing of the hen wild turkey. To produce the proper tone and pitch, the bone diameter must be just about right. A small hen seems to fulfill the specifications best, and the mature gobbler is much too large. Each end of the bone is cut off square, the interior is thoroughly cleaned of marrow and grease, and the ends smoothed with sandpaper. After the marrow is punched out of the bone with a stick or a pipe cleaner, I like to boil it a few minutes in water to which a little detergent has been added. This removes the grease, whitens the bone, and eliminates any odor or taste.

McIlhenny claims that the wingbone alone has caused the death of more wild turkeys than any other device. However, most hunters prefer to elaborate the caller somewhat. Some take the drumstick bone of a chicken and attach it with adhesive tape or a ferrule to the smaller bone to act as a bell or amplifier. The large bones in the first and second joints of the turkey wing can also be used for this purpose. Others attach a 12 to 16 inch piece of rubber hose to one end of the wingbone and the other end of the hose is fastened to a bell made from a cow horn. The piece of horn is held in the hand at waist level as the hunter sucks on the bone. The last 2½ to 3 inches of a cow horn is sawed off and about a 3/16 of an inch hole drilled through it lengthwise. Then with a rasp or reamer, the inside is hollowed out until the horn is quite thin. The tip is sawed off and worked with files until a slight knob is created to prevent the hose from slipping off, once it it attached over the end (see type VII).

There are other substitutions and modifications for the wingbone caller. The wingbone may be replaced with a piece of horn or solid bone drilled with a 3/32 of an inch hole. Good callers of this type can be made of three sections of bamboo (cane) which telescope into each other. The mouthpiece section should have a diameter of about 1/16 to 3/32 of an inch. Each of the other two should just fit the outside diameter of the next smaller one. The joints may be reinforced with metal ferrules and silk wrappings.

The Jordan caller is also of this type, with a wingbone mouthpiece and two sections of cane attached in the same manner. The original wingbone and all of these modifications are capable of producing all of the turkey language except the gobble. All are operated by sucking in the breath with the tip of the mouthpiece between the lips. Variations in tone, pitch, and intensity are produced by cupping the hands over the bell end, by sucking hard or easy, by moving the mouthpiece in or out slightly, and by using the tongue over the inner tip.

For those who do not care to make their own callers, a list of dealers is given below. Although there may be others in the country, these names are the only ones I have been able to locate in magazine advertising:

Inman Turpin, Sr., 3225 Spottswood Avenue, Memphis, Tennessee.

Tom Gaskins, Palmdale, Florida.

Roy O. Rhodes, Martinsburg, Pennsylvania.

Lohman Mfg. Co., 3801-03 East 18th Street, Kansas City, Missouri.

Herter's Inc., Waseca, Minnesota.

Philips S. Olt Co., Pekin, Illinois.

M. L. Lynch, 306 Edgewood Blvd., Birmingham 9, Alabama.

Phonograph records of turkey calling are sold by Inman Turpin and M. L. Lynch.

## Making Turkey Callers

*Simple box caller, or Yelper.* This caller is one which is simple to make, compact to carry, and quite easy to operate. For these reasons it is a favorite of many hunters and a sort of "standard" in many sections of the country.

Cedar, poplar, white oak, black walnut, and other fine-grained woods may be used for making this caller. Cedar usually produces the throatiest tone and makes the best imitation of the gobbler yelp. The other woods are likely to be higher pitched and produce the plaintive whine and yelp of the lost young hen.

Materials needed for this caller are: One piece of well seasoned wood (as listed above) 8 x 1 x 2½ inches; one piece slate 4 x ½ x ⅛ of an inch; sandpaper (No. ½); and soft chalk. The width of the slate scraper may be 1 3/16 of an inch if the hunter prefers the wider type.

Fasten the block of wood in a vice and lay out a pattern with pencil 6 inches by ½ an inch so that the one six-inch line is 1/16 of an inch from the smoothest-grain side of your block. Be sure to leave 1 inch at each end of the rectangle layout. In other words, center your six-inch rectangle on the eight-inch block. Mark a line lengthwise through the center of this rectangle and crossmark this line at ½ inch intervals. Then with a center punch, prick each of these intersections. Drill each of the marks with a ⅛ inch bit to a depth of 1 inch. Then with a ½ inch bit complete the drilling to a depth of 2 inches. The depth can be marked on the bit by wrapping it with a piece of adhesive tape. Be sure to hold the drill vertical so that it will not come out through the thin side.

Remove the remaining wood with a sharp wood chisel. Do not pound with a hammer. Get the bottom and sides as smooth as possible and then finish with a rasp and file. Thin the lip to at least 1/16 of an inch and perhaps less depending upon the tone wanted. When thinning for tone, only the upper ½ to ¾ of an inch need be filed. Finally, sand the box inside and out to make it as smooth as possible.

## HOME-MADE CALLERS

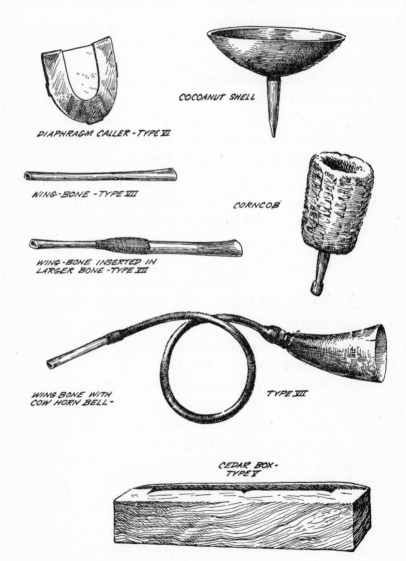

DIAPHRAGM CALLER - TYPE VI

COCOANUT SHELL

WING-BONE - TYPE VIII

WING-BONE INSERTED IN LARGER BONE - TYPE VII

CORNCOB

WING BONE WITH COW HORN BELL -

TYPE VII

CEDAR BOX - TYPE V

The slate scraper is sawed from blackboard slate or roofing slate with a hack saw. It can then be thinned and shaped with sandpaper.

To operate this caller, and any other box caller of this type, you should chalk the lip of the caller and the slate yelper thoroughly. Then the yelp can be produced in either of two ways. You can hold the box in the left hand with the sounding board away from your body and manipulate the scraper with the right hand. The scraper is usually held between the thumb and the middle finger. It is held almost at right angles to the top of the sounding edge, and the stroke is away and slightly downward.

Or the position can be reversed. The box is held in the right hand with the lip downward and toward your body. The scraper is held in the *cupped* palm between the ball of the thumb and the middle and fourth fingers. By putting the end of the scraper on both of these fingers and holding the other end deep in the hand, a deeper, more resonant note can be produced. The motion then is toward the body with the box tilted slightly backward from vertical. I prefer this method of using the box caller, because the yelps are more likely to be uniform.

When calling with a box caller, I prefer the purr followed with two or three yelps. To purr, the box is held almost exactly vertical to the scraper and pulled toward you with very little pressure. This is a slow, dragged-out note and high-pitched. Then the box is tilted backward and scraped twice or three times rather rapidly to produce the throaty yelp. The angle to hold the box or the scraper for best results will vary with the individual caller. Also, the exact point on the sounding board which will produce the best notes is variable. Usually it is near the dead center, but may be a little distance on either side.

*Another box caller.* For this one you will need a block of heart red cedar 6 x 1¼ x 1 3/32 inches. This should be a fine grained piece free from knots and cracks. On the wide side, hollow out a trough approximately 4½ inches long so that the sides and bottom are approximately 1/10 of an inch thick. This can be accomplished in the same manner as described under the directions for making the first box caller.

At the exact center of one of the sides, cut out a V-notch ½ an inch wide and ¼ of an inch deep. Then measure 1¾ inches each way from the center and cut out a notch at each of these points. This time, however, the notch should be a right triangle with base ¼ of an inch and the vertical line ¼ of an inch deep. The hypotenuse should face toward the center. Then mark off with a pencil a line between the two outer notches 1/32 of an inch in from the edge. With a fine file, remove the wood between the notches down to this line.

Next select a piece of fine grained heart red cedar for the top. This should be well sanded and smooth and measure 6 x 1½ x ⅛ of an inch. With a high grade of wood glue and clamps, cement this top on the box so that the excess lip sticks out over the side in which the notches were cut. Be careful not to get glue on the portion of the cover which will act as the sounding board. When thoroughly dry, dress the cover down with a file or sanding block. The back portion can be made very thin but the lip edge should be no less than 1/10 of an inch thick. The lip of the lid should be filed down so that it extends about 3/16 of an inch over the side of the box between the notches. From the notches to the end, the lip can be finished off flush with the sides.

The scraper is made of a piece of slate approximately 4 x 1 3/16 x ⅛ of an inch. Also, scrapers made of red cedar about 3 x ½ x ½ an inch are good. Either should be thoroughly chalked before using.

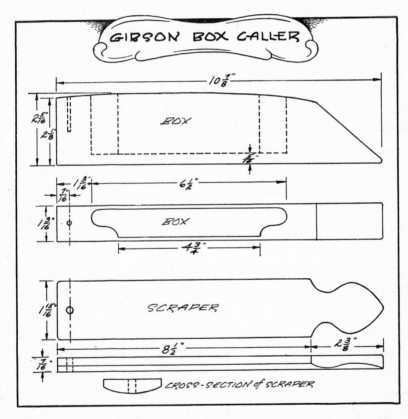

*Gibson box caller.* Red cedar is of little value for the Gibson. Most are made from poplar, but, as mentioned previously, Henry Davis made a good one from holly with an ebony cover. Probably other very hard, tight-grained woods would also be suitable.

For the main part of the caller, a block of poplar 10⅞ inches long, 2¼ inches wide, and 1 3/16 of an inch deep is required. The top of this block is made convex. Beginning at the front, the block is made 2 3/16 of an inch high and gently curved upward until it reaches a height of 2 5/16 inches at a point 2¼ inches from the front end. This height is held for two inches and then with another gentle curve is reduced to 2⅛ inches at a distance of 7 13/16 of an inch from the front. The front end and the bottom are cut at right angles and uncurved. The rear end, however, is cut at about a 45° angle, thus making the top shorter than the bottom.

In the convex top, a mortise is cut out with an overall length of 6½ inches. This is made to leave a uniform bottom thickness of 5/16 of an inch. This mortise is not regular as in the two box calls just described, but is cut so that the right side is 6 inches long and the left side is 4¾ of an inch long. The ends of the mortise on the right side (the 6 inch side) are round and ⅝ of an inch in diameter. This is joined to the 4¾ inch side with cyma curves (see cut).

The end of the mortise should be 1 3/16 of an inch from the front end of the box. The two sides which act as sounding boards should be about 1/10 of an inch thick at the top and a little thicker at the bottom. In the exact center of the top, 7/16 of an inch from the front, a screw hole is drilled for attaching the cover which acts as a scraper. This cover is 1 15/16 of an inch wide, 7/16 of an inch thick, and 10⅞ inches long. The top side of this cover is flat, but the underside is rounded to form a convex face for 8½ inches of its length. The remaining 2⅜ of an inch is used as a handle and is usually cut in the form of a rounded spear head. The rounded surface should be sanded with fine sandpaper (oo) until it is very smooth, The cover is attached with a long screw which is left protruding well above the cover so that it may be raised and tilted. The screw hole in the cover (7/16 of an inch from the end) is made large so that the cover may be manipulated freely.

The bottom side of the cover and the upper edges of the sounding board of the box are well chalked before using. The box is then held in the left hand (if you are right handed) and the lid tilted sideways and raised slightly. Then with a scraping motion the yelp should be produced— the hen yelp on the one side and the gobbler yelp on the other.

*Cocoanut Shell Caller.* There are no precise measurements for this caller. Mine are usually about three inches in diameter and about ⅞ to 1 inch in depth. This means that a small cocoanut must be selected, and preferably one with a thin shell. At any rate, by rasping, scraping, and sanding, the thickness should be reduced to about 1/16 to 3/64 of an inch. All fiber or soft material should be removed. In the exact center of the convex surface, about a 9/32 of an inch hole should be drilled. The area immediately surrounding this hole can be left a little heavier than the rest of the bell to support the peg a little better.

The peg is made of dead or seasoned mountain laurel (*Kalmia latifolia*). It is about 5/16 of an inch in diameter and about 2¼ to 2½ inches long. The upper end of the

peg should be tapered so that the end will enter the hole
easily but will fit tightly when about ¼ to ½ an inch is
pushed through the hole. The other end is tapered for about

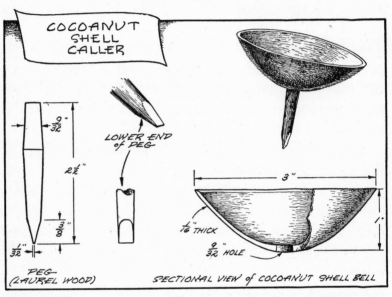

COCOANUT
SHELL
CALLER

LOWER END
of PEG

PEG
(LAUREL WOOD)

SECTIONAL VIEW of COCOANUT SHELL BELL

the last ⅜ of an inch so that the point is approximately
3/16 to ¼ of an inch wide and about 1/32 of an inch
thick. The peg is inserted so that the thinned edge is
pointed away from the convex (rounded) surface of the
shell. By wetting the end of the peg which fits into the
hole with the tongue, a tighter fit can be made. A tight
fit is essential for a clear and proper tone. The hole in the
cocoanut shell can also be tapered by using the handle
end of a six-inch file. The peg is removed to carry this caller.

To use this caller, the bell is held concave (hollow)
surface up in the right hand. It touches the first joints of the
three longest fingers on the one side and the inside of the
ball of the thumb on the other side. The hand should be

cupped so that the sound is not muffled. A square or round piece of slate about 2½ inches in diameter, or square, by about 1/16 to 3/64 of an inch thick is held in much the same position in the left hand. The tip of the peg is held on the slate, wide face in the direction of the motion, and pulled directly toward the user's body with a slightly curving stroke. The purr note is produced by holding the peg vertical to the slate and using little pressure. The yelps are produced by leaning the peg backward a little and applying more pressure. The slate and peg tip should be lightly sanded with No. ½ sandpaper before using. No chalk is necessary.

This is a good caller. It will produce a variety of yelps and the cluck. I have even heard a fair quality gobble imitated with a good one. Tonal quality and variation can be adjusted. Lengthening the peg will produce a lower note. Making the peg smaller in diameter will make higher notes. Thinning the bell will make the yelps higher and clearer.

A similar caller, and one of equal quality, can be made by substituting a thinned cow horn bell for the cocoanut shell. The peg of laurel is wedged tightly into the hole drilled into the sawed-off tip of the horn.

*Diaphragm Caller.* Instructions will be given for the construction of two breath-operated callers—the diaphragm caller and the wingbone caller. The first is simple to make. A piece of aluminum or other thin metal about 3 inches by 2 inches is required for the caller. This can be cut from an old sauce pan lid or other sheet metal.

The metal is cut in a long oval about 2¾ of an inch long by 1½ inches wide. This is folded in the middle making the finished product 1⅜ of an inch long by 1½ inches wide.

The center is cut out in an oval so that the remaining rim is ⅜ of an inch wide the whole way around the outside. This leaves an opening ¾ of an inch wide at the fold of the horseshoe-shaped holder.

When cutting the original oval, three lugs should be provided for in the pattern. One of these is on the extreme end, and the other two are about half way between the end and the fold line. These lugs, about ¼ of an inch long and ¼ of an inch wide are used to hold the folded halves snugly together. Once clamped, they keep the proper tension on the rubber diaphragm.

When the metal case has been folded so that the two halves coincide exactly, open it a little again and insert a small sheet of prophylactic rubber. The straight edge of the rubber sheet should fit in tightly against the fold so that it forms a straight line across the internal opening. Put just a little tension on the rubber without stretching it, and pinch the metal shut. Fold over the lugs, and your caller is finished. Of course, you will want to smooth the rough edges off the metal before you place the diaphragm in it so it will not irritate your mouth. Curve the caller slightly to fit the roof of your mouth. This caller is placed on the back of the tongue with the opening toward the front of the mouth. By elevating the tongue so that the caller is held next to the roof of the mouth, it comes into calling position. Then with the proper puffs from the throat and lungs, the yelp and other notes are produced. This is one of the very best, but requires practice.

*Wingbone Caller*. This caller has already been sufficiently described so that the hunter will be able to construct one or more of its variations. Because of the simplicity of the caller, there is no need for detailed instructions. One additional hint which might be offered is that a cork ring can be cemented in place around the wingbone near the tip to act as a guide for the lips. This will assure the hunter that he has the call placed in the same position each time he calls with it. In this way he is less likely to make off-color notes.

To use the wingbone caller, it is well to cup one or both hands partially over the bell end. This will help modulate the tone and pitch. The sound is produced by a smacking or kissing motion while the user is sucking in his breath. By varying the length of each yelp, the time interval between, the pitch, and the quavering quality, the yelps of both hen and gobbler and the lost notes of the young birds can be reproduced accurately. The cluck is made by placing the tongue over the opening and jerking it away as the breath is sucked in sharply. Only practice and imitation of wild or domestic turkeys in the flesh can make the hunter proficient in the use of any caller. A good phonograph record is a wonderful aid, also.

### Clothing and Miscellaneous Equipment

There is still a strong argument among turkey hunters about the need for wearing dark clothing which will blend well with the surroundings. Some are convinced that even the tan-colored coats, trousers, and hats made from duck cloth are a definite handicap until they become weathered and dirty. Others argue that color means little, but it is the brightness of the shade which counts.

It appears that most wild mammals are more or less color blind and that they only see different shades of gray from black to white. Deer, for example, appear to pay little attention to bright reds, yellows, and other colors, or even to the brilliant fluorescent shades. I have had deer, on several occasions, walk right up to me when I was wearing a fluorescent cap and fluorescent safety vest over my coat. From their actions, I could just as well have been a stump. Biologists have found, however, that birds appear to be attracted by grain of a certain color and repelled by the same grain dyed other colors. This information has been used when poisoned grain is put out in fields for mice and other rodents to prevent killing beneficial birds.

There have been few if any controlled experiments to determine the frightening effect of different colors on game animals. I personally question whether the brighter colors in the darker shades would be a handicap to the hunter. Particularly in the fall, there is a riot of color of all kinds in the forest anyway. If the birds were going to react violently to every splash of red or yellow they saw, surely they would be nervous wrecks during the autumn months.

As long as we have "trigger-happy Harrys" in the woods, there is always a real danger to the hunter who does not wear some protective coloration. Too many men have been filled with shot when they were sitting in underbrush and using a turkey caller. A colored cap or some color on the coat seems to be good insurance. It is suggested that the turkey hunter experiment during the off season, in conjunction with his scouting and practicing on the turkey caller, to see just how allergic the birds are to different colors. And when the hunter doesn't have a gun along, he can afford to let them walk right up to him.

Another consideration in the selection of hunting clothing for wild turkeys, deer, and other alert game animals is to choose cloth which won't squeak or whistle as you walk along. Some hunting trousers made of stiff, hard duck and other hard-woven cloths will make a loud swish-swish as one pant leg passes the other. If a man is making all kinds of other noises as he walks through the woods, this matters little. But if he is walking quietly down a woods road, or on snow or wet ground, this noise can be a real handicap. A guy can stop it if he walks bow-legged all the time, but it is much simpler to buy trousers made of softer materials. Brush striking against a duck hunting coat is also noisy, and this can be eliminated by wearing a woolen coat or one made of soft cloth.

A handy gadget to have along when turkey hunting is a web-strap carrier. These birds may weigh twenty pounds or more and are no fun to tote out of the brush just carried any old way. The strap with a metal V at one end certainly lightens the load. A ¾ or 1 inch rawhide strap can also be used. About an inch from one end a slit 1½ inches long is made so that a loop can be formed by running the other end through it. The loop is slipped over the head of the dead turkey and the feet are tied with the other end. The bird is then slung across the back with the strap running diagonally across the chest. In emergencies, a handkerchief can be used to tie the feet together.

The final essential piece of equipment is a pocketknife. Under certain circumstances, it is desirable and necessary to hog-dress a turkey in the field. The reasons will be given later.

# Chapter 9:

## Attributes of a Successful Turkey Hunter

A MAN who wishes to be consistently successful in his wild turkey hunting should acquire certain attributes.

He should have thorough knowledge of wild turkey habits and behavior characteristics. He should understand their daily routine and how this is sometimes greatly affected by weather.

He should be intimately acquainted with the territory in which he plans to hunt. By pre-season scouting he should locate one or more resident flocks and determine where and on what they are feeding. He should acquire sufficient woods lore so that he feels at home in the forest and can keep from getting lost. He should know how to read "sign" and how to travel with as little noise and excess movement as possible.

He should be adept with the turkey caller.

He should be a good shot, and be able to estimate distances and leads accurately.

He should carry a rabbit's foot.

### Knowledge of Turkey Habits

I have many times heard hunters say, "You've got to be smarter than a turkey to kill one." This is obviously not always true, but it does help. If a man knows next to nothing about the life history and habits of wild turkeys, his chances for bagging one are going to be mighty slim. He will not know when and where to hunt, or what to do in case he blunders into a flock. He should know what they eat, when they are most likely to be feeding, where birds are most likely to go in search of food, where they roost, what effect different kinds of weather have on them, and many other things. Some of this information can best be obtained by spending a lot of time in the particular area to be hunted, but a lot of general information can be learned which will apply to almost any territory.

One of the best things to know is where the birds are feeding and what they are eating. In ridge or mountain country, there is often quite a difference in the kinds and amounts of mast produced in the valleys, on the slopes, and on the tops. In the oak country of southern Pennsylvania, the bottomland will have white oaks mixed with pin oaks, red oaks and a variety of hardwoods other than oaks. On slightly higher ground, the white oaks give way to scarlet oaks, black oaks, and red oaks. On the steep, rocky upper slopes and tops, the chestnut oak may occur in almost pure stands. Farther north, the transition will be similar but with northern hardwoods instead of oaks.

Because the amount of mast produced by the various fruit-producing trees, shrubs, and vines varies greatly from year to year, the turkeys are likely to be found feeding where food is most abundant. If only the chestnut oak produced well during any particular year, the hunter would do well to work the tops of the ridges. When there is an acorn failure and the turkeys are feeding on dogwood or grape, the old slashings and grape tangles would be the "hot spots". When one of the rare beech crops occur in the northern hardwoods, the turkeys will be found on the large beech flats on the tops of the plateaus. At other times, the black cherry may be the mainstay in the turkey diet.

Turkeys are easiest to find and kill during years of natural food shortage. At these times their feeding range may be greatly restricted simply because in most places there is little to eat. During the season of 1953 in Pennsylvania, there was a marked shortage of mast in the northern part of the state. In some sections, the "sun side" of the high ridges, just under the rim, were literally covered with grape vines. These were blue with grapes, and a flock of birds, sometimes two, could be found every day feeding on this fruit.

The very next year, there were plenty of acorns and very few grapes, and the turkeys were exceedingly difficult to locate. Under those conditions, the birds could feed almost anywhere and were scattered all over that big county. The kill was poor until a good tracking snow came along.

In the South and Southwest, the same is often true, although the food supply does not vary so greatly in warmer climates. But even there, the hunter should know what the preferred foods are and where they grow.

By careful observation and study, the hunter can figure out where turkeys are likely to be found. In the same manner he can determine when they are most likely to feed. Nearly all game birds have two major peaks of feeding activity—for a couple of hours after daylight and for a couple of hours before dark. Turkeys are no exception to this rule but hold to it less rigidly than many of the smaller species. Because turkeys have relatively few natural enemies and depend upon their keen eyesight for safety, they are not afraid to remain active throughout the day. Therefore, a flock may be found walking and picking at almost anytime during the daylight hours unless it is extremely stormy, extremely cold, or extremely hot.

When food is scarce and the birds are working one thing very hard, such as the grape thickets, then they are most likely to be found there during the early morning or late evenings. Of course, one hunter a few minutes or a half-hour ahead of you can easily flush the birds out of the feeding grounds and have them moved a mile or more away by the time you arrive.

Weather has a great effect upon wild animal activity. During severe snow storms, turkeys may remain on the roost for several days without coming to the ground at all. During heavy rains, they may stand around listlessly for long periods at a time. And when there is a deep, soft snow on the ground, they are likely to spend a large part of their time in trees for a day or two. This is because it is almost impossible for them to walk when they are practically sinking out of sight. During droughts or just ordinary dry weather these birds will be forced to go to water at least twice daily. In the West, this is particularly important.

So, a knowledge of the normal daily activity or routine is a great aid to the wild turkey hunter. But he should also know how weather restricts or changes their daily habits so that he will be prepared for the unusual, or will know enough to stay at home.

### Familiarity With the Country Being Hunted

The second attribute of a successful turkey hunter is given in the above heading. This is just as important to bagging a turkey as it is to know the birds' habits and behavior characteristics. For one thing turkeys are not too much unlike deer, bears, foxes and many other animals. They, too, have more or less regular crossings and travel lines. This is particularly important to the "still hunter" who is sitting with his back to a tree hoping that a flock will walk past him. There is nothing more discouraging to a hunter than to be waiting in the wrong spot day after day.

How do you find out where these travel lines are? The answer to that question will reveal the real secret of success for a great majority of wild turkey hunters. In fact it is the only way that the novice or the mediocre hunter is ever going to qualify for that enviable class known as "the experts." The answer is simply that the hunter should repeatedly scout the country he expects to hunt. Naturally, pre-season scouting pays off best, but much valuable information can be gained at any time of the year. In the North, a lot can be learned by following tracks in the snow during the winter months.

Travel lines in the mountain areas are likely to be along the sides of the slopes and parellel with the top of the ridges. The level of travel must be determined from observation and experience. Sometimes a "bench" part way up the side of a mountain forms a natural travel line. At other times they may follow the lower slope where it begins to flatten out into a wooded valley. In the swampland of the South, the high ground areas or hammocks are the logical travel ways.

Low "sags" or saddles in ridges are common places for flocks to cross from one side to another. They also like to go around the point of a ridge where it ends or is broken by a water gap. It should be remembered that these travel lines are ordinarily dependent upon where the food supplies are during that particular year and where the birds go to escape when disturbed by hunters.

In good turkey country, pre-season scouting of the hunting territory will sooner or later turn up the feeding and traveling ranges of one or more flocks. As soon as these flocks are located, it is not difficult through observation to discover where they are feeding and what they are eating. The hunter should then decide whether this particular food is seasonal in character and whether it will perhaps no longer be present by hunting season. Or if it is not a short-term food item, he should decide whether there is a sufficient supply to last into the hunting season.

Early season scouting for other kinds of game is often misleading. Black bears, for example, may be working a particular region hard during early fall when a certain nut crop is present, but will move out almost completely when the supply is exhausted. The hunter who goes into this region during the late fall will be greatly disappointed because the animals will have disappeared. Although turkeys will not move out of an entire township like bears will, they will change their habits and range sufficiently to disrupt the well laid plans of a hunter. For this reason, scouting done immediately prior to the opening of the season is likely to pay the greatest dividends.

## Acquired Woods Lore

Too few modern hunters are woodsmen. As a matter of fact the average nimrod of today hesitates to get out of sight of his car for fear of getting lost. He charges through the woods sounding like a herd of elephants, and sees nothing unless it flies or runs right out in front of him. He has little patience and less fortitude. He most often is in too big a hurry to take the time to become proficient at his sport. He would prefer to blunder along with the hope that some turkey will make a foolish mistake or that some bird frightened by another hunter will fly over his head. He tries a caller or two but gives up when he can't get sweet notes within the first few minutes. Or he does just the opposite, and squeaks and squawks all over the woods and drives every self-respecting turkey (and turkey hunter) into the next county. He carries any kind of gun, but probably an open bored twenty, and shoots 2's and BB's through it. Then he

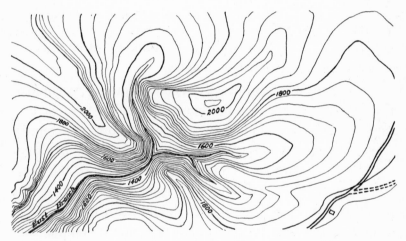

*When hunting strange country, utilize a topographic map.*

does not hestitate for a moment to try a gobbler at ninety yards. And last but not least, he is the guy who complains about the scarcity of game, and damns the Game Department for giving the hunters nothing for their license money.

If a hunter uses his head, there is little excuse for getting lost. In the first place, a man who is not completely familiar with the territory should spend thirty cents and get a topographic map of the area. These can be bought locally at sporting goods stores and other stores, or from the U. S. Geologic Survey, Washington 25, D. C. The Survey will furnish a master sheet for any state, and the hunter can pick out the map name for the locality where he wishes to hunt. These large scale maps (1 inch equals 2000 feet or 1 inch equals 1 mile) show streams, roads, trails, forested areas, openings, elevations (contour lines), swampy areas, and many other topographic features. With one of these maps, a man can plan his hunt, and, with reasonable caution, should never get lost for long. They are great for planning a hunt in strange territory, and an old turkey hunter in new country can save himself miles of walking oftentimes by scanning the map for a few minutes.

Almost anywhere in heavily wooded country, a compass is a valuable asset unless the hunter is willing to stick to a single drainage in mountainous terrain or knows the country well. There are woodsmen who can travel all day in almost any direction without a compass and not get lost, but these are the exception. A few dollars spent for a compass is a good investment and the hunter should learn how to use it properly. This instrument is of little value unless the user knows what direction it is back to camp or car.

The real woodsman can use Nature for a direction finder. He can keep himself located by the sun, the wind, the difference in vegetation on the various slopes, and in many other ways completely unknown to most hunters. Just last year a member of our deer hunting party was lost all day and until three o'clock the next morning. He knew he was hunting south of the highway, but had no compass and had no idea which way was north. This, in spite of the fact that a strong north wind had plastered snow up against the trees all day long. The south sides of all trees were bare and black, and the north sides were covered with an inch or more of snow. How simple it would have been if he had kept walking toward the black trunks, instead of spending most of the night wandering around in the bitter cold.

Even when the sun is obscured, a knife blade point held on a watch crystal will usually cast a shadow and act as a compass. The north slopes of ridges will usually have a different type vegetation than the south slopes, because they receive less sun. Even the vegetation on the south side and the north side of an individual tree may vary, and sometimes the north sides of trees will have lichens or fungus growths not found on the sunny side. The wind can be a usable direction finder most days, although a marked change in weather during the day will sometimes indicate a change in wind direction as well. The topographic map will often show a general direction of flow for streams. And it will show the location of roads, trails, and land prominences which might be used as direction finders.

It has been pointed out again and again in these pages that the wild turkey is a smart bird. It has extremely acute vision and a highly developed sense of hearing. Yet the average hunter comes close to ignoring both these facts. When he travels in the woods he does so at top speed and with no particular care about where he places his feet. This is how *not* to kill a turkey. The successful turkey hunter has learned that it is better to take a half-day to walk a mile or two than to cover ten miles at a rapid gait. He uses Indian stealth in his movements and takes advantage of the topography and the cover to mask his movements and to hide his walking sounds.

Like the Indian tracker, the turkey hunter should be able to read sign. He should notice and recognize droppings, shed feathers, dusting sites, scratchings, tracks in mud or sand, and other indications of the presence of birds. He should be able to tell whether the sign is fresh or old. He should be able to recognize the slightest turkey sound, even the low clucks and putts. He should be able to pick out the still form of a turkey in the woods and distinguish it from the stumps or snags nearby. He should *be* an Indian.

Still another attribute of the successful turkey hunter is being able to use a caller well. Very few of the mechanical calls will reproduce the desired sounds unless they are operated expertly. It takes years of practice to master most musical instruments, yet many hunters give up in complete disgust when they cannot become proficient on a turkey caller in a few minutes. Practice, practice, and more practice makes the good turkey caller. He sits at the domestic turkey farm and answers the calls of the tame birds, or the lucky one may even live within a reasonable distance of game farms where the real wild bird is raised. Or he can buy a recording of the different calls and imitate them again and again.

The real test is in the forests. In late summer or early fall, the enthusiastic caller can locate hens with their broods and learn many things talking to the young birds. Or they can go out in the spring in states which do not permit spring shooting, and learn the language of the old gobbler and the young bachelor. He will learn more out of season without a gun than he will in season, because then he will be willing to experiment and play with the birds as they continue to respond instead of shooting them at the first opportunity.

The caller should be used at intervals throughout the year so that certain "feel" won't be lost. Long continued practice sessions in the homes are sufficient grounds for divorce, but there are times when the lady of the house is away.

There is going to be no attempt here to tell the turkey hunter how to shoot. If a bird has been called in or is just walking by the still hunter, there is little need for expert shooting. Just hold on the head and neck and squeeze her off. If the bird is flying, it is a different story. The wild turkey, once in full flight is one of the fastest game birds. A bird flushed from the top or near the top of a mountain and headed steeply downhill will probably be travelling close to 60 miles an hour, maybe more, by the time it has flown a quarter of a mile. Two years ago one of these dive bombers went directly over my head at about 60 to 65 yards off the ground. The bird had its wings set and the air rushing through the stiff wing feathers made a buzzing sound which could be heard for at least 150 yards each way. I held fully 25 feet in front of the big fellow and shot just once, but he never faltered. I suspect I should have made it 40 feet.

The rule then for pass shooting on turkeys when they have their wings set and are gliding downhill would be to lead them as much as you would a wild duck at the same range. If the bird is still flapping or has taken off in level flight and has set its wings, it should be led much as you would a ruffed grouse, bobwhite quail, or ring-necked pheasant under similar circumstances. It will fall into the 30 to 40 mile per hour class then.

Many hunters expect their shotguns to kill at impossible ranges simply because they have no conception of distances.

It will pay any new hunter and many of the older ones to measure off some distances in the woods and then examine them carefully. Try 40, 50, and 60 yard ranges if you are shooting anything no larger than a standard twelve gauge. Add the 70 yard distance for the twelve magnum. Also, it will be wise to pattern your gun and determine in that manner how far you should shoot. When you can no longer put at least six or eight heavy shot in a ten inch circle, then you have exceeded your effective killing range. Birds which are crippled to die later are doing no one any good and are a waste of a valuable natural resource. Also, you are actually cheating someone else out of an opportunity for some precious recreation and the thrill of bagging one of these magnificent birds. When you shoot, shoot to kill, or don't shoot at all.

*Chapter 10:*

# Methods of Hunting

## *Calling*

IT IS ASSUMED that every turkey hunter, in order to get the greatest possible pleasure from his sport, will want to learn to call these birds. The first portion of this section will be devoted to general information about calling wild turkeys, the second will tell how to imitate the various calls and notes, and the third will describe methods and techniques for hunting specific ages and sexes of turkeys at different times of the year.

To call wild turkeys successfully, a hunter needs to know four things in particular. First, he must be able to produce a sufficiently good imitation of "turkey talk" to fool the birds. Second, he must know when, and when not, to call. Third, he must know where to call or call from. And last, he should know what to do after he gives his call, especially once he has the turkey started toward him.

It is somewhat difficult to say which of these four requirements is most important. Any one, if not done properly, can offset the other three. No matter how adept a man may be with a caller, he still will not kill many turkeys if he does everything else wrong. On the other hand, with all other precautions carefully followed, the man who is only mediocre with a caller may have some success. It must be remembered that distance and wind can mellow many sour notes, and that the turkeys themselves often make a great variety of funny noises, too.

Except in certain specialized forms of turkey hunting, for example, the calling of old gobblers during the spring mating season, the first requisite to successful calling is to scatter a flock. Turkeys are gregarious; that is they prefer to travel in the company of other turkeys, and will try to reassemble as quickly as possible once they are separated from each other. By calling back and forth to each other, they soon get together again. The hunter, by imitating these call-notes, can attract birds to him, one at a time. When the turkeys are intact in the flock, they are contented, and will rarely respond as a group to the call of a lone bird. The flock may answer, but they expect and insist that the lonesome, lost individual come to them rather than they go to it. This is quite reasonable and logical. Only in the very early fall when most of the flocks are composed of families of young birds will they occasionally go to the lost call of a youngster.

The main idea then is to locate a flock and get it scattered. Of course, locating the flock is usually the harder job, and this can be done in several ways. If a roosting location is known, the hunter can be in the vicinity before daylight and perhaps hear the birds as they leave the roost and start feeding. Or he may merely keep walking slowly and quietly and hope that he will come upon one. Or he may have a tracking snow in the northern states. At any rate, however a hunter may locate the flock, he wants to get it scattered well.

Usually it is difficult to walk or run close enough to a flock of real wild turkeys to get a good shot with a shotgun as they flush, although there are many exceptions to this rule. If you are lucky enough to do this, they will almost certainly fly or run to every point of the compass, whether you kill one or not at the flush. But normally, they will be beyond shotgun range when you first see them and usually they will see you at the same time.

The best procedure is to start shooting the moment they see you to frighten them as badly as possible. If they are sufficiently disconcerted by this effort, they will scatter in all directions and one or more may even fly right back over your head. When they fly off in every direction, this is the ideal situation for the hunter who wishes to call. Sometimes, however, he may not sufficiently startle the flock to produce this effect. Then the flock may pick up pretty much as a unit and fly in a fan in one general direction. If the whole band lights within a radius of two to three hundred yards, they may reassemble in a matter of minutes and clear out of the country on the dead run or at a fast walk. In this case the hunter can only hope that he may run across them under better circumstances later in the day or go hunt another flock.

But let us suppose that the flock has been scattered in good shape. Now what should the hunter do? The most important thing of all is that *he should stay right there.* Novice hunters will often try to follow the largest segment and attempt to call them a quarter or half mile from the place where they were originally flushed. This procedure is not too dependable because the birds are often content to return to the assembly point singly and will make no particular effort to join with others on the way. Therefore, the hunter may get answers to his yelps, but be disappointed when the birds walk right on past him out of sight or out of gun range.

So, pick a good spot within fifty to seventy-five yards or less of the place where they flushed and prepare to call. Now there are several precautions which should be considered in picking a spot to call from. The first of these is to select a place that will permit the hunter to see a bird when it comes within range. In other words do not bury yourself in a thicket so that any turkey which may respond to your call will be out of sight unless he walks right up to you. Many turkeys will not approach closer than thirty to fifty yards, and a good opportunity can many times be lost because of this oversight. Also, the hunter should be careful not to locate himself in the open about fifty to seventy-five yards from some thick, extensive cover. Nothing is more exasperating than to have a turkey come readily to your call from a quarter of a mile or more away and then refuse to leave the thick cover and come out into the open within shotgun range. It is best to keep at least 150 yards from this kind of cover if possible. Wise old birds which will come to the call but stop and refuse to come any closer when they are just out of shotgun range, can be fooled by tandem hunting. The man calling places his partner fifty yards or more in front of him. Then, when the old bird begins his marching up and down, he finds soon enough that he is not out of range of the lead man.

Many an expert hunter merely sits down with his back against a good-sized tree, and when he gets an answer he pulls his hat down over his eyes, raises his knees to hide the remainder of his face, and holds his gun in readiness over his knees. If the weather is warm, this position seems to be satisfactory, but because he is unprotected the hunter dares not move without jeopardizing his chance to kill a turkey.

He is better off to stick a few leafy branches into the ground in front of him and thus hide most of his minor movements. Or better yet, he should sit inside a natural blind of brush or a fallen treetop where he can safely move about a little to prevent cramping and chilling. He should never get behind a tree so that it is necessary to stick his head around the side to see the turkey or to point his gun.

This brings up another point, however. Wherever callers are used to imitate turkeys, there is always the possibility that some careless or unsportsmanlike hunter will sneak up and throw a charge of shot into the brush where he thinks a turkey is standing. This certainly proves his ignorance and game-hoggishness, but, nevertheless, this type of hunter always will remain a threat to the man who hides himself too well when calling. Screen yourself, but don't bury yourself in the brush. Be particularly careful about visibility from the rear. This is your really dangerous side because you are less likely to see anyone approaching from that direction. On quiet days a man should be heard walking in the leaves for some distance, but when a wind is blowing the danger is greatly increased.

In a later chapter on calling the old gobbler during the mating season, the hunter is cautioned not to call too much. This applies to a certain extent at any time. When an old tom is gobbling and strutting in the spring, he is used to having the hens come to him. Once he has heard you and has your location, it is extreme folly to call anymore. As long as the hunter calls, the old gobbler will stay in one spot and continue to strut and wait expectantly. But if he hears his lady friend no more and thinks she has lost interest in him, then he is likely to walk over to investigate her lack of enthusiasm. Even in the fall, every fifteen to twenty minutes is often enough.

The rule of thumb to follow is to stop calling as soon as you have an answer and the bird is on its way. Even if the bird does not appear for an hour, the call should not be repeated under most circumstances. Of course, young birds and sometimes even older birds can be "talked in" the whole way without alarming them. But it should be remembered that one false note is usually sufficient to spoil everything. The man who keeps calling should have a lot of confidence in his ability, and even then he is probably gambling needlessly because the bird would normally come just as readily without the extra effort. If the bird happens to stop coming and appears to be getting farther away, then try to imitate its call exactly and it should come on in.

But, as usual, there are exceptions to all rules. For example, a turkey may come almost within range and stop and cluck. If you do not answer, it will think that the bird is gone or has been frightened away by some danger, and will come no nearer. If you do answer, it will come on in without hesitation, unless in your excitement you hit a false note. This is why wild turkey hunting is so fascinating!

Sometimes, too, a turkey called from a long distance may slightly misjudge your location, although this is rare, and walk past you just out of range. A cluck or low yelp will turn it to you. It is better to call and turn your bird than to chance a long range shot as he walks by. Even a loud yelp or two at short range will not alarm a bird if it is executed properly. Two years ago, I peered cautiously over the rim of a mountain and discovered a flock of turkeys feeding within forty to fifty yards below me. I had already killed a turkey and was not permitted more by law in that state. Close to me were three old bearded gobblers feeding in a little clearing at the foot of the steep slope not thirty-five yards away. I just remained squatted and admired these beautiful specimens as they scratched and fed. Every bird was dragging his beard in the two-inch snow, and certainly they were all at least three years old.

Just out of curiosity, I pulled out my box caller and gave three low hen yelps. All three heads came up immediately, looked a moment or two, and then they went back to feeding. Encouraged, I yelped louder, and repeated again and again. Although, they would not leave the flock to come any closer, they never showed the slightest alarm, and I was exceedingly pleased that I had passed the test so well. If these old patriarchs could be fooled, surely the others could be. I left this flock without their ever knowing that they had a visitor.

Speaking of turkey beards reminds me of a discussion some of my hunting companions had one day on the way home after a hunt. Proving the old adage "the first liar never has a chance," one of the boys told about seeing an old gobbler that day with a beard so long that he kept tramping on it as he walked. Another one spoke up immediately and said, "You think that's a good gobbler! The one I saw today had a beard so long that the bird behind him kept tramping on it!"

Old gobblers in the fall and winter and young gobblers in late winter are prone to be silent. Oftentimes they will respond to the call of the hunter and start his way but will make no sound themselves. Many hunters will move as soon as they call and receive no answer. Others will sit a few minutes, call once or twice more, and then move before the old fellow gets to them. These wise old gobblers often cautiously circle and carefully inspect the surroundings when they get near. If the hunter should stand up to move or make any other pronounced movement, the old bird would disappear in a flash. In all probability, less than half of the turkeys started to a call are ever seen by the man doing the calling. It pays to stay put at least a half hour after calling when turkeys are known to be in the close vicinity.

In heavily hunted states, a hunter may have little difficulty getting an answer to his call. If an answer continues from the same position time after time and gives the same notes repeatedly, there is a good chance that the bird is another hunter trying to call you. But be sure. So many times when you are so positive that you are being duped, a big old turkey walks out into view. Or when it sounds too perfect to be anything else but a real wild turkey, you find that you have run across an expert turkey caller. The real unhappy state occurs when one good hunter calls, gets an answer from another good hunter, and then both sit, and sit, and sit waiting for the turkey to come.

On windy days, the hunter should call very loudly and keep very still. There is little chance that he will hear the turkey answer and he must be constantly on the alert for a bird to walk into sight. I have had the experience of standing up, after calling into a high wind for fifteen or twenty minutes, and have a bird flush within thirty or forty yards. These birds were undoubtedly yelping at intervals but the sound was blown away before it reached my ears.

Another hint on calling, which is worth a lot to know, is that the birds should be called uphill in mountainous or hilly country. Normally, turkeys walk uphill and fly downhill. In heavily hunted areas, flocks will be scattered time and time again before the season has progressed very far, and single birds might be found almost anywhere. Under these circumstances, a good method of hunting is to work the upper slopes or rim of the ridges or mountains and call every few hundred yards. If the day is calm and sound is carrying well, every quarter-mile may be often enough. If a wind is blowing, it may be necessary to stop every hundred to two hundred yards. For real success, the hunter should call from above where he thinks a bird might be feeding or loafing.

Sometimes when a turkey is higher than the hunter, it will fly below the call and run back up to it. Or sometimes it will fly in and light directly behind the man doing the calling. But most often they refuse to come down, even though they may answer.

It was pointed out in the very beginning of this chapter that the most important requisite to successful calling was to scatter a flock so that the individuals could be called. Sometimes, however, there are complications even in this. As a general rule, but certainly not infallible, flocks scattered before mid-afternoon will try to assemble yet that day, but if scattered later they will usually not try to get together until the following morning. From this it is obvious that it is not always necessary for the hunter to scatter his own flocks. Some other hunter may have done it earlier in the same day or in late afternoon of the previous day. In either case, the birds would be separated and ready for calling without the necessity of hunting up an intact flock and attempting to scatter it.

Sometimes the hunter is faced with the decision as to whether he should "bust up" a flock which has already gone to roost in late afternoon or early evening or wait until the following morning at daylight. Tom Turpin advises that if the hunter is using a rifle, he can shoot and turkeys will fly in every direction because they cannot pinpoint the sound. In this case, two or three are likely to fly back over the hunter or light in the trees near him so that he will have an opportunity to kill one.

However, if he fires a shotgun, they are more likely to fly away from the hunter and light in the trees. And even though he return at daylight the next morning, he may not have any success. Tom Turpin's experience under these circumstances is that the old hen will cluck a time or two just before daylight and fly some distance away. The rest of the flock and will see her go and follow. Of course, this is assuming that the trees are bare. If they are still in leaf, there will be much calling before the flock assembles. Only when they cannot see each other will they call to any extent.

If the birds are left undisturbed on the roost the afternoon before, then the hunter should be there before daylight the next morning and scatter them. If they remain in the trees, he should follow them and keep driving them out. The main thing is to keep them separated until sunrise when all that are still in the trees will fly down to the ground. Once they are on the ground, and separated, then calling should be good.

Occasionally a flock may be flushed in open country, particularly in the South. If they leave the opening and fly into the trees beyond, the hunter can, by running at top speed, run right under the trees where they are sitting. He must start immediately, not stop on the way, and expect to shoot the second he stops. If he is able to hold steady after a long, fast run, collecting a bird should not be too difficult.

And now a hint or two about what to do after you have shot at a bird. A broken-winged turkey will outrun any man if it has good going and is not hurt otherwise. When you shoot a bird, particularly out of the air, get to the spot as quickly as possible. Sometimes a few seconds can mean the difference between losing a winged bird and having a chance to shoot it before it can run out of range. If a leg is hanging when the bird flies away, try to mark it down as closely as possible. Go to the spot and hunt carefully for it. It will not go far from the spot where it lights, and will probably crawl into some thick cover. Or it might light in a tree. At any rate, it can usually be flushed at close range and killed on the wing.

Whenever you shoot at a bird, with either the shotgun or rifle, watch and listen because it may collapse after it gets some distance away. Sometimes these large birds can be heard falling through the limbs and onto the ground at quite a distance. Or they may be seen to collapse in full flight and come tumbling to the ground as much as three or four hundred yards from where they were first shot.

This final bit of advice is offered to the turkey hunter. Never forget the cardinal rules of hunting safety. In a few instances, it has been recommended that you run, but be sure that your gun is "on safe" before you do. Be sure of your target before you pull the trigger. More than one hunter has been shot for a wild turkey! And never, never assume that a hidden call is a real wild turkey. It may be

an expert hunter hidden behind the brush. No real sportsman will take a chance on "sound shots."

It should be remembered that the information on hunting
given in this book applies countrywide. In only a few states
is it lawful to hunt in the spring; other states permit only
gobbler shooting; still others have restrictions on certain
devices and equipment, and many limit the daily shooting
hours. All readers are urged to secure a digest of the state
game laws and become familiar with the regulations applying to wild turkeys in that state. It pays to obey the law.

*Imitating the Various Turkey Calls and Notes.* There are
six different classifications of calls or notes in the wild
turkey language. These are the cluck, the alarm putt or pert,
the yelp, the whistle or kee, kee, kee of the very young
bird, the gutteral roost call or tree yelp, and the gobble of
the mature male. If the hunter wishes to master all of the
different calls of possible use in hunting turkeys, he is con-
fronted with the task of learning eleven. There are sex and
age variations in pitch, tone quality, loudness, and inflection
for most of the call notes much as there are in human
voices. As a result, he must learn three clucks—young hens,
old hens, and gobblers; and five yelps—young hen, old hen,
young gobbler, old gobbler, and the love yelp of the hen
in the mating season. Naturally, he will not want to learn
the alarm putt, and it is impossible to imitate the final call—
the assembly yelp of the mother hen.

Each of the various calls will be described.

## The Yelp

The plain yelp is the most common of the many calls in
the turkey language, and it causes the death of more turkeys

than all the rest of the calls put together. The yelp can be used successfully at any season of the year, if the proper one is used. The various yelps can be produced by almost all types of callers and are the easiest of all for the novice hunter to learn.

The hunter should learn to recognize the yelp of the old hen trying to call her brood together, but should not attempt to imitate it. The young birds know their own mother's voice and will not respond to that of another hen or to any attempted imitation on a caller.

This call is very unusual and not too difficult to identify. She will yelp fifteen to twenty times loudly and rapidly, and then her voice will deepen and the last few yelps will be lower and more prolonged. The hen will seldom move about when she is thus signalling her brood. These calls will be repeated in quick succession until she apparently runs out of breath, and then she may pause a minute or two and start in again. If the hunter wishes to kill any of her offspring, he had best chase her away as soon as he is sure that it is a mother hen, and then return and call to the young birds with the kee, kee, kee, whistle. Sometimes the mother hen will call her brood with a long series of cluckings, again from one spot, and may continue for an hour or more if her offspring do not join her.

All of the other kinds of yelps can be imitated, and will produce results under the right circumstances. The love call of the hen in the mating season is a soft, low, quavering yelp given very rapidly. This is usually given as either two or three notes. The yelp of the young hen in early fall is high pitched, usually more of a high whine than that of the males and older hens, and contains a plaintive, "where are you?" quality. The hen notes are likely to be in a rather fast rhythm—*keouk, keouk, keouk,* but the gobbler's yelp will be more widely spaced and held longer—*keouk—keouk—keouk.* Later in the winter the young gobbler's voice will change so that his yelp becomes more of a hoarse *croc, croc.* The old gobbler, if he yelps at all, will also give a coarse note, sometimes so deep and vibrating that it sounds at a distance almost like the bark of a dog.

The final yelp is the one described by Tom Turpin as the "tree yelp." It can be used as a method for locating turkeys while they are still on the roost very early in the morning. The yelp is coarse and muffled as though the turkey had its head down a well. The notes are drawn out longer than in any other kind of yelp. When making it with the wingbone type caller, the hands should be cupped over the end and the sound should arise deep in the throat. The three *keouks* should be drawn out and about three seconds allowed between each note.

## Clucks

The clucks are used as assembly notes or as a means of asking questions such as, "Where are you?" or "Are you still there?" The cluck may sound like a note which would lack any particular character, but there are male and female clucks, and old and young clucks. Sometimes turkeys will respond to clucking when they will pay little attention to yelping. Extreme care should be taken, however, to imitate the cluck or "cut" exactly. It is so close to the alarm "putt" or "pert" that one false note can frighten your bird away.

The cluck of the hen is made on a wing-bone type caller by placing the tip of the tongue over the hole in the end of the wing bone and releasing it with a jerk as suction is applied. The cluck of the young gobbler is somewhat the same, but is more like a mixture of a cluck and a yelp. It is made with strong, quick kissing action of the lips and sucking action of the breath. The young gobblers will often use it to answer your yelp or other call. Only through hearing it in this manner can you hope to imitate it expertly, so every effort should be made to impress it on your memory.

### The Lost Call of Young Turkeys

Wild turkey poults give a lonesome, plaintive whistle when lost. This is usually a clear, high-pitched run of six or seven notes and seems to carry the inquiry, "Where are you, Mother?" This call can be imitated very closely just with the lips and mouth, and is an excellent call for early fall hunting. However, by November the birds are sufficiently matured that the whistle has changed to coarser, whining notes but still in the same rhythm. This can also be imitated fairly well by the mouth, but a better, more perfect and louder note can be produced with the wing-bone type caller.

This call is by far the best of all for hunting young birds of either sex in the fall. It is superb for attracting single birds of a scattered flock, and it is one of the few calls which will actually bring a whole flock to the gun. Again, it is impossible to describe the notes sufficiently well so that a hunter could go out and reproduce the necessary sounds. He will have to hear a young bird whistle or whine before he will be able to master the notes and rhythm of the call. A game farm, a domestic turkey farm, or a scattered late summer flock of wild birds should be the answer to this problem.

The wing-bone caller or the diaphragm caller are the best for this purpose. The notes should be practiced without a caller. The rhythm and general tone should be mastered by whistling it with the lips at first. Then if the wing-bone type call is to be used, the several kee, kee, kee notes should be made while breathing in one long breath. When this can be done easily, the caller may be substituted and the whistled notes imitated. By varying the position of the tip in the lips and by cupping the outer end, the proper tone and pitch can be achieved.

## Gobble

The gobble is exceedingly difficult to imitate by means of mechanical callers. Some few men are able to do a passable job with their own vocal cords, but these are few and far between. The diaphragm caller and the cocoanut shell caller will also work fairly well. The gobble is seldom used effectively in calling turkeys and there is little value in attempting to master it. Sometimes it can be used successfully to decoy the young gobbler in late winter after he has deserted the hens.

## Calling the Old Gobbler in the Mating Season

Calling the gobbler during the breeding season is perhaps the most difficult and most trying of all. He is old and wise, and is accustomed to having the hens come to him. He is not anxious to chase after a hen which stands off in the brush somewhere and calls. As Tom Turpin says, the real secret of success in this case is not so much what to do but what not to do. Of course, this technique applies only to the Southern states which have spring "gobbler" seasons.

One thing the hunter must be very careful about is to be sure that he gives the hen yelp and not the young gobbler yelp for obvious reasons. The love call of the hen is sufficiently different from the young gobbler call that most hunters should have little difficulty with it. The hen's call is soft and low, but is delivered snappily. Two or three of her vibrating, quavering yelps are all that should be given. The young gobbler call is more drawn out with longer intervals between yelps. In using the wing-bone type call, the lips are closed tightly and the sound is produced by a smacking motion much like kissing. This should be done jerkily with the lower jaw working up and down. The young gobbler yelp is made with longer, smoother sucking efforts, with greater intervals between each *keouk*.

One of the surest ways to bag the old gobbler in the spring mating season is to be near his roosting site before daybreak. This should be before the first awakening noises of the day. Just about the time the first crow calls or the first birds sing, the old gobbler is likely to give forth with his first vocal effort of the morning. If he happens to be non-talkative, he can often be stirred into gobbling by an imitation of the hoot of the barred owl or the great horned owl. If a bird answers the owl call from a roost at some distance, the hunter should try to get as close as he can to the roost without disturbing the bird. With experience, you can tell about how far away the bird is. You should walk something over half the distance and hoot again. By stopping and hooting three or four times, you should be able to approach to perhaps within a hundred and fifty yards or less of the roost tree. But great care should be taken not to get too close and "spook" the bird.

In place of the owl hooting technique of locating a gobbler, the hunter can use his caller entirely. You should arrive before daylight as before, and at the right time try a cluck or two, a low yelp, or the "tree yelp." If no gobbler answers, move to a new location about "hearing distance" away and call again. By doing this repeatedly, you can cover a large territory and should locate a bird sooner or later.

The best opinions seem to be that it does not pay to try to call a gobbler out of a tree. He expects the hens to come to him, and may remain in the tree just so long as he thinks a hen is coming. You should not answer his gobble by yelping. Probably a cluck or two and a low yelp, just loud enough for him to hear, is all that should be given while the bird is still in the tree. Sometimes he will fly down directly to this call and light within a few feet of the hunter. At other times he may strut and gobble on his limb for some time before flying down. Once he does reach the ground, your success and how soon you succeed will depend upon several things.

You may have him coming to you, usually leisurely with repeated struttings, when a hen comes to him. This means at least fifteen minutes delay before he has taken care of his marital duties and the hen has left him again. Then if another hen has not appeared in the meantime, he may continue his slow approach. When you hear a hen come to your gobbler, do not call again for at least fifteen to twenty minutes. Then call just enough to restore his passion, which the hunter can recognize by the increased tempo of his gobbling, and then stop calling altogether. This time he may come, or another hen may interfere. Perhaps it will be an hour or a half a day before you finally have him within range. Or he may never come at all.

Sometimes the old fellow may be distracted or uninterested in your call and begin to wander off in another direction. Then it is advisable to leave your place and make a long detour and get in front of him. If he has not seen nor heard you, he should answer your "love call of the hen" with a gobble, and start toward you once again.

Sometimes an old gobbler has so many lady friends that it seems almost impossible to lure him away from them. Then an entirely different strategy may be the answer. If the hunter can locate the old tom the first time he gobbles, he should approach within about a hundred and fifty yards and circle the roosting tree at that distance with the intent of frightening away any of the hens in the harem. The hens will usually be found roosting some distance from the old male. When the hens are flushed, their direction of flight should be noted, and then the gobbler's tree should be approached from that side with the hope that he will fly in the opposite direction. If he can thus be separated from the hens and chased into territory where he is not accustomed to gobble and strut, the task of calling him to the gun will become much easier. The hunter should immediately close in on him somewhat. Within twenty minutes to a half hour the old fellow should be sufficiently settled and calmed so that he will respond to the caller. And now *you* have the advantage, because he is disturbed and lonesome and anxious to rejoin his ladies.

*Calling the Young Gobbler in Late Winter*

When the gobbler of the year is still with the family flock in early fall, he is as easy to call as the hens, once the flock is scattered. However, later in the year when the sexes have separated, these independent youngsters become very difficult to call. In the northern states where the seasons are confined to a month or two in the fall, this does not apply because it is not until December or later that the young gobblers begin to leave the hens. From this time on, they will not respond to the hen yelp, and can only be called by imitating the yelps or clucks of the young gobbler itself.

This may seem simple enough, but unfortunately these notes are difficult to imitate. His voice lacks the clearness and resonance of the old gobbler, and sometimes it may not sound like a turkey at all. His yelp has been described as a hoarse and discordant croak and the cluck like an acorn falling into a pool of water or striking the loose bark of a log. They usually seem to lack interest in anybody or anything in general, and are likely to ignore your calling in silence. In fact, the young gobbler at this time of year may be fully as reticent to answer as the older gobblers. However, once he has decided to come to you, he will march right along with little hesitation.

Sometimes the young gobbler will become separated from his flock for several days and be very eager to find company. His call at this time may be loud and clear and full of excitement. He is eagerly hunting companionship when he utters this call and may move rapidly from place to place. He will often respond to a yelp or two, or a cluck, by dashing toward the hunter on the dead run. This is when turkey calling seems easy.

### Calling Wild Turkeys in the Early Fall

In the more northern states, the hunting seasons usually fall within the months of October, November, and December. The hunting period is most often one to two months in duration. During October and early November, a large part of the birds in the forests are only sixteen to twenty-four weeks old. At this age they still retain some of the characteristics of the young poult. For example, when the family flock is scattered by a hunter, the young birds evidently feel very lonesome and insecure and desperately desire to rejoin their mother and brothers and sisters.

For this reason, they are the easiest of all to call. Even the rankest novice, scraping out a yelp of sorts on a box call, may have one of these youngsters walk, or run, right up to him. They are actually lost and frightened and are more than willing to share the company of any other turkey, regardless of sex or age. As a result, they are likely to respond to almost any of the great variety of calls described earlier. The main requisite here is that the notes sound like they were given by another turkey and not like the discordant squawks and screeches which so often emanate from the callers of the uninstructed hunter.

The best call of all for working with young birds of the year is the lost call of the young bird. The kee, kee, kee, whistled with the lips in October or produced on the wing bone caller or diaphragm caller in November and December is almost sure fire if done well. About six or seven of these kee, kee notes in a run is best. The first note is low and not so loud as the rest. Then as the run continues, the notes get higher and are dragged out more. Each one is a little more plaintive and desperate than the one before, and the whole call has a rising crescendo and inflection as if the bird were saying please, please, please, PLEASE, PLEASE, PLEASE.

The common hen yelp or cluck and the lost call of the young bird will suffice to bring in all birds with the possible exception of the old gobbler. It may be necessary to imitate his coarse yelp or cluck to have real success with him. And remember, it is better to call too little than too much for these old reprobates!

## Still Hunting

There will always be an argument between those who prefer to still hunt and those who prefer calling as to which method of hunting wild turkeys requires the greater amount of skill. Certainly each demands plenty of knowledge concerning the bird and its habits and of woodcraft in general. I am of the opinion that the expert caller must be born with some inate ear for turkey music and then be willing to master the mechanics of the instruments he uses through long practice and patience. He might be termed a virtuoso because of his skill with an instrument which in a broad sense is musical. He also must learn a language just as difficult and foreign as French or Russian. The expert turkey caller might be thought of as an artist-hunter.

The still hunter, on the other hand, should be born a natural woodsman with many of the attributes of the early American Indian. He must learn to walk quietly through the forests and to use the vegetation and the natural topography to keep himself hidden much of the time. He must learn how to stalk his game and to find it in the first place through his ability to read "sign" and to track his quarry.

He must have an intimate knowledge of the characteristics of the bird he is hunting and how to use this knowledge to outwit his clever adversary. The expert still hunter is not an artist perhaps, but certainly he is a craftsman.

Still hunting for wild turkeys literally means just that. Turkeys have acute senses of sight and hearing. Probably the keenness of their eyesight is almost unexcelled in the animal kingdom. The eagle has been credited with the most extraordinary eyesight among birds, but it must be remembered that he is up in the air looking down where seeing is easy. Put the eagle on the ground in the forest, and chances are he would be ten times as easy to stalk as a wild turkey.

The wild turkey's hearing is also acute but far from infallible. All sorts of things can distort or mask sounds, so that hearing ranks well below its eyesight as a means of protecting itself against its natural enemies or against hunters. Its sense of smell appears to have almost no value as a warning mechanism.

Obviously then, the still hunter needs to keep quiet and to keep from being seen if he is to expect success. This applies when he is just walking through the forest, when he is making his stalk after sighting birds, or when he is sitting and waiting for a flock to walk to him. It is difficult to instruct anyone on the subject of how to walk quietly. However, there are a few very important rules to follow which will help, and proficiency will be gained only through practice and experience.

Probably the first and foremost essential toward quiet traveling in the forest is to *go slowly*. Remember, if you are still hunting and not intending to use a turkey caller, the next one hundred yards is just as likely to produce a flock of turkeys or a single turkey as another hundred yards a mile away. You should sneak along in exactly the same manner as you would if you knew that there were birds immediately ahead of you and you were actually stalking them. You should be doing just that at all times if you expect results.

It hardly seems necessary to say that the hunter should watch where he is putting his feet so that he will not tramp every dry branch and twig on the way. Set your foot down toe first and gradually lower your heel. With a shoe or boot which is not too heavily soled, a stick of some size can be felt under the instep as the foot comes down and your weight can be held on the toes for that step. Continued practice will make you another Daniel Boone, but remember— *go slowly*. You will kill more turkeys walking a mile in this manner than you will in walking ten miles sounding like a herd of elephants coming through the leaves and brush. Needless to say, these tactics will help you kill your deer during the deer season as well.

As you sneak along slowly, the turkeys ahead are less likely to notice your movements, particularly at longer distances. But this is normally not enough precaution against being seen before you see them. For one thing you will probably be outnumbered—a dozen or more pairs of eyes against your one pair. For this reason, it is essential that you use the vegetation and the topography as cover to keep yourself out of sight a large part of the time.

My favorite method of still hunting in Pennsylvania where the turkeys are found on mountains and ridges is to hunt the rim. Most Pennsylvania mountains have fairly steep to very steep sides and flat tops. In the Appalachian region in the southern part of the state, the ridges and mountains are long and narrow, and the tops are often only a few feet to a couple of hundred yards across. Rim hunting is at its best here but is also valuable in the Alleghenies which have much broader tops.

The idea for the still hunter is to get on top of one of these ridges and walk along it parallel with the ridge. If the hunter walks back fifty yards or so from the rim he cannot be seen by anything down over the side nor does the noise he makes in walking carry down. You should travel along slowly and carefully, because the turkeys can be on the top as well, for perhaps one hundred or one hundred and fifty yards. Then sneak out very, very carefully to the rim and look down over the side with as little of your head and shoulders showing as possible. Inspect every inch of the terrain below you for at least five minutes without moving. If you see nothing, return to your original position back from the rim, walk on for another hundred or more yards and repeat the process. If the top is narrow, this can be done on both sides as you progress along the ridge.

In relatively flat country, locating birds without "spooking" them is far more difficult. But the same general principles apply here as well. Every little depression or rise should be used as a natural blind, and the hunter should approach such places with great caution and carefully peek over, into, or beyond these irregularities. I recall many instances wherein I have deliberately or accidentally walked right onto a flock of birds and had them rise all around me, simply because I suddenly popped over a rise or down into a natural basin. This is one of the most spectacular and long-remembered experiences a hunter can have in the great outdoors. To have a dozen or twenty of these giant birds take wing within a few yards of you, with the attendant wing flapping, perting, and squawking, is truly a spectacle. And then to pick out a bearded gobbler and drop him just as he clears the treetops is the fulfillment of many a hunter's dream.

The hunter on quiet days should spend a lot of his time listening. He should walk a few yards and stop to listen. A feeding turkey just walking through dry leaves may make nearly as much noise as a man, particularly if it is not anticipating trouble. However, a suspicious bird can be very quiet even in dry weather. When several of these birds are scratching in the forest litter, the rustling and scraping can be heard long distances. And then there is usually the murmer of the family discussion—the low clucks and muffled yelps of the contented flock in conversation as it moves along. So listen, and listen carefully, for these audible indications of turkeys ahead. And be suspicious of any unusual noise; it may be turkeys. But DON'T SHOOT at suspicious noises.

*Reading "Sign."* Reading sign is often exceedingly helpful in locating turkeys and even for determining whether it is a family flock of young birds and hens or a few old gobblers traveling together. The presence of turkeys in an area may be denoted by scattered feathers, droppings, dusting sites, tracks, and scratchings. The hunter should learn to recognize all of these indications and to know what they signify. The wing, tail, and body feathers of a dead bird should be studied so that a loose feather found in the forest can be identified without hesitation if it came from a wild turkey. Note the black and white barring on the wing feathers, the mottled brown of the tail feathers, and the iridescent hues of the body feathers. If it is a breast or back contour feather, it will also indicate which sex dropped it.

Dusting sites may be found along the edges of clearings, on old woods roads, and even in ant hills. These are usually large, the size of a dish pan in circumference. If the loose earth in the cup-like depression is examined, it is common to find one or more feathers. This should verify whether it really is a turkey wallow or one made by a ruffed grouse or other large game bird.

Droppings are typically worm-shaped and curved and usually larger than a lead pencil. Few hunters have not seen the droppings of domestic turkeys or of chickens and should recognize them with little trouble. Those of the grouse are smaller and often found several in one place, either on the male's drumming log or where the bird roosted overnight. Wild turkey droppings are usually mostly dark green to black in color with a white tip. The white part is the solid urine excreted by birds and the dark portion is the feces from the large intestine. Turkey droppings are most often found along old roads, the edges of fields, around forest openings, or where food is particularly abundant in some small area.

Tracks of turkeys should be mistaken for few other birds. Perhaps in the deep south where large wading birds utilize the same areas, there could be cause for confusion occasionally, but even then there should be little difficulty in distinguishing between the two types of foot prints. Snow makes the ideal tracking medium and no one has trouble following a bird under these conditions. Sometimes when the snow is several inches deep and soft, the novice may have trouble determining which way the birds are headed.

This is usually easy, however, if you know how. The turkey drags his feet and will often make a tapering line with the nail of his middle toe (the longest one) in front of each track. This little groove points the way he is going. Also, on wet snow the hunter can dig down very carefully and actually see the footprint and get the line of travel.

Tracks can be found in the mud and sand on or alongside roads, trails, and edges of fields. Although these will be im-

*The bird is traveling in the direction the V scratching points.*

possible to follow, they at least denote the presence of birds, and their comparative freshness will indicate how long ago the turkeys passed that way. However, you can't eat tracks!

Scratchings are the best "sign" of all for still hunting turkeys on bare ground. Like other birds of this group, wild turkeys kick and rake through the leaves with their feet to turn up nuts, seeds, insects, and other items of food which might be buried under them. Both young and old, male and female, scratch in this manner, but the experienced woodsman can often determine age and sex, how long ago they were made, and in which direction the flock was moving.

Suppose you come across some scratchings in the forest. The first thing you should do is examine them for freshness. If they are very damp in the bottom and still literally "steaming" then you may be in trouble. There is a good chance that you have frightened the birds as you approached and that they are now several hundred yards away and still on the dead run. If the soil and forest duff is still damp in the pockets formed by the scratching but showing signs of drying somewhat, then the chances are that the birds are not too far away and may not be spooked. If the scratchings are dry and look weathered, then they are probably at least a day or two old. Remember that hard rains or winds can alter their appearance very readily and fresh scratchings can look old quickly. If the weather stays dry, they may at first glance look reasonably fresh for a week or more, but a close examination of the bare ground in the center of the depression will reveal that a lot of drying has taken place. The hunter can be fooled by scratchings made in late afternoon or early evening, because these may appear very fresh the next morning.

DIRECTION OF TRAVEL ➡

To decide which way the birds were traveling is comparatively easy. The leaves are always kicked backward and the apex of the V is forward. The feet are kicked outward and backward so that each depression left is wider at the back

than at the front—much like an inverted V. If the scratchings are few and not widely scattered in a line, the chances
are that a very few birds are ahead of you. If the forest
floor is rooted up like a bunch of hogs had been feeding
there, and they cover a strip fifty yards wide, there is a
large flock.

Now what kind of birds were making the scratchings?
Sometimes the damp earth uncovered during these feeding
efforts will contain a track or two. If the span from the end
of the largest (middle) toe to the end of the hind toe is
more than 5¼ inches, it is a gobbler. But the feet of young
gobblers are almost as large as those of old gobblers, so this
alone will not necessarily indicate a flock of old toms. There
are ways of telling whether you have found a family flock
of mixed birds or a group of old gobblers, however. For one
thing, if a hen track is found in any of the scratchings you
can be sure that it is a family flock. If tracks are scarce, then
look for other signs. For example, old gobblers like to scratch
around the bases of trees, often times right up between the
root ridges. Their scratches are very large, often as much
as two feet across, and their long and powerful legs and feet
may throw the leaves five or six feet to the rear. The toe
marks are large and wide apart, and their droppings are even
extra large in comparison with those of the hens. Also, they
have a tendency to keep walking at a faster rate, and their
scratchings will be more widely spaced along their route
of travel.

Before leaving the subject of scratchings, it might be well
to point out that the tyro can often find turkey scratchings
even when there are no turkeys in the country. Deer paw-
ings, squirrel diggings, hog rootings, and the scratching of

song birds are most likely to be confused with the real
McCoy. When the old buck is in a fighting mood during
October and November, he will often stand and paw with
one front foot much like a mad bull. And while he is doing
this he may be grunting and snorting his defiance to the rest
of the bucks in the world. Without examination, the inex-
perienced hunter could mistake this bare spot for a single
turkey scratching. But the buck almost invariably digs right
down into the ground, sometimes a couple of inches or more
deep. And the broad grooves made by his split hoof are
easily distinguished from the toe scratches of the turkey.
A full-size standing hoof print can often be found on the
bare soil. And sometimes a freshly rubbed tree will be found
nearby where he stood and polished his antlers.

Squirrels will make scattered little *round* pockets in the
leaves seldom more than a foot in diameter. In the center of
these will be a small hole dug down into the soil from which
a nut has been retrieved or in which a nut has been buried.
Only by chance will any of these have the typical V shape
of a turkey scratching.

In the South, wild hog rootings are common but their
tracks and the deepness and thoroughness of the turnings
can leave little doubt in any hunter's mind about the origin
of this work. In some sections, small ground working song
birds will scratch up sizeable areas under seed producing
trees. I have seen this particularly under dogwoods, iron-
woods, witch hazel, and others of this type. Even though
the spot will have a thoroughly stirred appearance, the small-
ness and shallowness of the individual scratching will easily
identify the maker.

*Stalking.* Suppose as a still hunter you have located a flock, either by sight or by sound, or you are following fresh scratchings on bare ground or fresh tracks on snow. Now comes the last, and perhaps the most important, part of the game for you.

If you are following fresh scratchings, proceed with extreme caution. Walk very slowly, scanning the woods ahead of you with great care. Remember you must see them before they see you. Take advantage of any ravine, ridge, or thicket to hide yourself as you follow them. And now suppose that you are fortunate enough to spot the flock a hundred and fifty or two hundred yards ahead. If you know anything about turkeys at all, you will know that it will be impossible for you to get within shotgun range as long as they are in fairly open timber. Of course if you are carrying a scope-sighted rifle which shoots a high-speed cartridge, then you may want to try your skill right then and there. Or you may want to get behind a natural screen of vegetation or a hump in the terrain and creep up another fifty yards or so on your hands and knees or belly before you touch her off.

But let's assume that you have your shotgun today. Then what is the procedure? Abandon the idea of sneaking up on them from behind unless there is a perfect opportunity presented by some paralleling ditch or ravine or other natural cover to hide behind. This is seldom present, however. The thing to do is to watch them for a little while. First, make sure they are going, not coming. At that distance, unless you have field glasses, you will not be able to tell whether they are facing toward you or away from you except by the difference in general coloration. When one or two birds straighten up, look them over carefully. If they look black they are facing you, but if they appear light gray or brown in color they are facing the other way. Very soon you can decide which direction they are headed and plan to cut them off. Wait until they feed out of sight, then withdraw carefully, and make a wide circle of the flock and sit down two or three hundred yards ahead of them and hope that you have accurately estimated their line of travel. If they pass out of range, you will have to try all over again. This technique will work for a single old gobbler or lost youngster as well as it will for a flock.

If you are following tracks in the snow, the same procedure may be followed. Once your birds are sighted, sneak around in front of them and wait. This is called "bush-whacking," but it still requires plenty of skill and patience.

I have several times had the experience of catching a flock in thick cover, particularly in Pennsylvania wild grape tangles. I have known of many hunters to sit for an hour or two on the outer edge of one of these tangles with the hope that sooner or later they would show themselves. Many times the birds would eventually work out the other side and be lost, simply because the hunter was afraid to move for fear he would flush the flock and get no shooting. This leads me to my favorite expression about wild turkey hunting: "The reason that most hunters fail to bag a wild turkey is because they either underestimate or overestimate the intelligence of the bird."

Under these conditions, where the cover is thick, do not hesitate to walk right into them. Walk as quietly as possible, and keep your head down, but keep moving. In fact, I believe that running may be the best bet in many cases. The birds cannot see anything because of the denseness of the vegetation, and they have no way of identifying the noise exactly. It could be another turkey, a deer, a squirrel, or a dozen other things, and the typical reaction is to "freeze" and wait to see what it is. As a result it is not uncommon to find that you have walked right into the center of a flock and birds may get up singly or in two's or three's all around you. This makes delightful shooting when there are no restrictions on sex.

Just two years ago I had this experience and estimated that I had a choice of nine different easy shots before the flock finally got out of there. In Pennsylvania, too, the birds will often fly from the top or side of one ridge or mountain across the intervening valley to the side of another ridge. If this is densely clothed with mountain laurel, as it often is, the hunter or hunters can cross over and walk back and forth through the laurel as if they were hunting rabbits or ringnecks. Very often the birds will squat in this thick cover, and flush out at close range just like a grouse. This is particularly true at the beginning of the season when the young birds lack experience and are thoroughly frightened. The same idea is applicable in any thick cover whether it be pines, hemlocks, cane, rhododendron, or even thick weeds. Not uncommonly, rabbit hunters will flush turkeys out of dense weed cover in old fields adjacent to turkey timber. These birds may be out there in early fall chasing grasshoppers or they may just run out of the woods and attempt to hide when pressed by hunters.

In summary, if you find your birds in open timber when still hunting, get in front of them and wait for them to walk to you. If you hear them in thick cover, give them the bum's rush and get your bird on the wing.

The only remaining form of still hunting is the "just sittin' and waitin'" kind. This is real bushwhacking. You sit around in the woods where turkeys are known to be working and hope they walk past. Or you sit at the edge of a field where they have been feeding or around a grape thicket, a water hole, or some other spot to which they have been coming regularly. Or some locate a roost or two and sit near it morning and evening. This is the lazy man's way, and requires little skill but much patience. This is not the kind of wild turkey hunting for me.

Three more hints to the still hunter before we leave this chapter. If he manages to locate a flock and gets shooting but fails to kill his bird, he should locate himself in the close vicinity where the flock was scattered and sit there for several hours if necessary. The flock will try to reassemble near the same spot, and there is a good chance that he will see one or more birds in the next two or three hours.

The second word of caution is to be careful of gun barrel glint in the sun. Nothing will ruin your chances so quickly as a flash from a bright gun barrel. If the bluing is becoming worn and the steel is exposed, the spot should be darkened by new bluing, by smoking or by staining. When sitting and waiting for turkeys, the hunter should stay in the shade so there will be less chance for this barrel glint to frighten his quarry.

The final hint is for still hunters who like to hunt with one or more companions. Usually the group scatters the first thing in the morning, unless they have already located some birds the previous day, and each man goes his own way in an attempt to find a flock. This is best in many respects. In the first place if two or three men walk along together, they make that much more noise and are just that much easier seen. And they are not going to see any more than one man, if as much. So to get widest coverage and the greatest chance of getting into game they should scatter in different directions or parallel each other two or three hundred yards apart.

But the important thing is this. Suppose one of the group finds a flock and perhaps scatters it. He wants to signal his companions to come over his way and get into the thick of things. There is no better system of signalling than the hunter's horn which can be heard for several miles on a quiet day. If one man gets into turkeys and wants his companions to come to him, he blows three blasts on the horn. They answer with two blasts to signal that they are on the way. If anyone wants to know where the other man is, he blows just once and the other answers with one blow. This way they can keep in touch, and it is of value in preventing someone from getting lost or in locating them in case of an accident.

These hunting horns are made from cattle horns and can be bought or made at home. For those who wish to make their own, just get a fair-sized horn from a cow or bull, cut off the solid tip, drill the right sized hole through the cut end, and insert a bugle or trumpet mouthpiece. A little scraping, sandpapering, and polishing will dress it up for you.

### Hunting Turkeys With a Dog

I have never had the privilege, if it could be considered a privilege, of hunting turkeys with a turkey dog. And I probably never shall, because this is rapidly being outlawed in most states. Davis considers this practice meat hunting purely and simply, and suggests that it requires little or no real hunting skill, except shooting ability perhaps. Although I can appreciate working with a well trained dog as much as the next sportsman, I personally feel that far greater satisfaction can be derived from calling or still hunting this particular kind of game.

My second-handed description of turkey hunting with a dog is not intended to provide instructions to the hunter, but rather to point out some interesting facets of the sport. For one thing, a dog if well trained can make this extremely intelligent bird appear stupid, and makes it very easy prey to the hunter. Because of this, the uncontrolled use of dogs where hunting pressure is heavy could mean the end of good turkey hunting and perhaps the end of the turkeys.

In general, dogs are used only in the fall and winter months. They could be used during the gobbling season but probably less effectively on singles than on flocks. The dogs used are most often pointers or setters, but the Scotch and Fox terriers and certain of the spaniels are also effective. Hounds are also very good, provided they are silent trailers. Many plain mongrels are also excellent when trained.

Some hunters use their dogs only to find and scatter a flock. Then with the dog lying silently at their sides, they call the turkeys in the usual fashion. The only other aid the dog might then give would be in retrieving or holding cripples. The dog should be taught to grab and hold a turkey by the head or neck only so that the body skin and flesh will not be torn and made less presentable for the table.

More often the dog is used even more effectively. It locates a flock through sight or scent, and then dashes into it barking madly. This will put most or all of the turkeys into trees. It will then follow them and bark "treed." The hunter, armed with a scope-sighted rifle, then sneaks up close to the spot where the dog is barking and picks off one or more. The birds are usually so intent on watching the dog that they do not see the hunter approach. It is possible at times for a good shot to get several birds when a flock is treed. This is why the widespread use of dogs could be dangerous to the future of turkey hunting.

Dogs used for hunting turkeys should not be allowed to chase other forest game. And it should be emphasized that the dog must remain silent until right on the birds. If it barks too soon or barks on the trail for some distance, the flock may remain on the ground and run for miles without flying into the trees. Or the whole flock may rise and fly together for a half mile or more. The surprise and confusion of the last minute dash is what causes them to scatter and tree.

McIlhenny warns that the repeated use of a dog on a flock will eventually drive them out of that territory.

In the West, greyhounds have been used to chase and catch turkeys in the open country. The hunters follow on horses.

Speaking of hunting wild turkeys with a dog, reminds me of some of my early work with the wild turkey. As a research biologist assigned to a wild turkey study in Pennsylvania, it was my duty to live with a flock of newly released game farm birds to attempt to find out what happened to them. For several weeks, I would be at the roost where I had put them to bed the night before, follow them at a distance all day, and then put them to bed again. Later, I attempted to keep my eye on several flocks of stocked birds and would attempt to locate as many as three or four of the releases daily.

To aid in this work, I used my old coal-black setter who originated as the result of a cross between an Irish setter and an English setter. He was an old work horse who had been used for everything from censusing all kinds of game birds to locating escapes from the game farm pens. He would stand staunchly on point while a net was flopped over an escaped bobwhite, ringneck, or other bird, and then walk away disinterestedly as soon as he saw the bird struggling in the net. He had another trick which further proved his unusual discernment. He would trot along the edge of the pheasant holding pens completely ignoring the hundreds of birds just inside the wire, and would lock up on an escape or a wild single not three feet away and stand there fifteen minutes or more if it didn't move.

While working with the turkeys, he was my constant companion and quickly learned the vagaries of this new bird. He would range widely through the forests and if he did not return after a long cast I would go hunting for him. Almost invariably I would find him on point, often as much as seventy-five to a hundred yards from the flock. Most often he would locate them by sight and quickly freeze, and neither birds nor dog would move until I appeared on the scene. He surely saved me many extra miles of walking, and undoubtedly added much to the success of the study. I hope one day to have another somewhere near as good.

*Chapter 11:*

## Field Dressing Your Trophy

U NDER certain conditions it is not necessary to field dress a wild turkey to preserve its flavor or to prevent it from being spoiled for the table. If the weather is cold, there is little chance that the flesh will be tainted from bacterial action. And if the bird is empty or has been eating cereal grains or certain nuts only, the crop may not have to be removed. And if the bird is not shot through the intestines, there is less need for field dressing.

But for safety, the crop and the visceral organs should be removed as soon as the bird is killed. If the turkey has been eating certain vegetation or fruits with a strong odor or taste, this will rapidly be absorbed into the flesh as the bird cools. Therefore, the crop should be removed if it contains food. This can be determined by pinching the area at the base of the neck where it enters the breast. The crop lies underneath at this point and may be larger than a baseball when full. Slit the outer skin over the crop for about four inches, being careful not to cut through into the crop itself. and then remove the sac containing the food in one piece. Then for fun, open the crop and try to identify the food items.

Keeping the bird on its back, cut a lengthwise slit from the end of the breast bone almost to the vent. By inserting two fingers into the opening just in front of the vent, the large instestine can be straddled with these fingers. Then by lifting slightly, the vent can be circled with the knife and the end of the large intestine freed without getting any of the feces inside the bird. Reach the hand into the body cavity and grasp the gizzard, which will be the large, round organ, and pull it loose. This will remove the gizzard and all intestines. Then reach back in and remove the liver and heart. On the underside of the liver will be the green gall bladder. Cut this away, being careful not to spill its contents on the liver. When they say "bitter as gall," they mean it. Next cut the intestines away from the gizzard, and make a lengthwise slit along the outer edge extending about half way around the circumference. Again be careful not to cut through the inner skin which holds the food. You probably will anyway, so open it up, dump out the contents, and remove the inner lining by starting it with the thumbnail and then just pulling.

Little else need be done except to use common sense about refrigeration. No meat can be permitted to hang in the hot sun or lie in a car parked in the sun for half a day or more and expect it to remain fresh and good. At least keep it in the shade or as cool as possible until you get it somewhere where it can be refrigerated. It will not hurt a turkey to hang for several days with the feathers and head intact provided it is kept cool and has been properly field dressed.

Final dressing can be done by you or your butcher. The feathers may be plucked dry but they pull rather hard and the skin is likely to be torn unless considerable care is taken. It is preferable to scald it in hot water (not boiling) just until the feathers loosen. If the bird is going to be held in a deep freeze for some time before it is used, the hot water bath should be about the right temperature to prevent over-scalding and a reddened condition of the skin called "freezer burn." Most commercial turkey markets hold their hot water bath at about 140° Fahrenheit.

*Chapter 12:*

## Cooking The Wild Turkey

I HEAR so many people say that they don't like venison, or rabbit, or wild ducks, or wild game in general. This disturbs me because I am of the opinion that there is no finer meat in the world than wild game, if properly cooked. I also believe that there is no worse meat in the world than wild game if not properly cooked. My conclusion then is that most people who register a distaste for it have never eaten properly cooked wild game.

It's peculiar, too, because some of the best housewife cooks in the world are often most guilty of ruining game in the oven or on the top of the stove. I have seen people make a ritual out of broiling or frying T-bone beefsteak and insist that it be cooked just so. But give these same people the choice loin steaks out of a deer and they fry or broil it until it looks and tastes like sole leather. Then they say, "I don't know how you can enjoy that stuff." Frankly, I couldn't under such circumstances. But broil or fry it on a hot fire, sear it quickly, and serve it rare to medium rare, and these deer steaks can equal the finest T-bone found anywhere.

The same is true with rabbits, squirrels, woodchucks, and other small game animals of this kind. Some people parboil them two or three times in salt water, draining the meat and adding new water each time. They even add soda, vinegar, and other ingredients to "kill the wild flavor." They certainly accomplish this, because they wind up by killing *all* flavor. I wish someone would explain to me what

wild flavor is anyway. After a great many years of eating
all kinds of wild game I have yet to find any with a "wild
flavor," with the possible exception of some east coast ducks
which have been feeding on the sewage flats downstream
from some of the big cities. Fish eating ducks also fall in
this category.

But upland game birds or mammals seldom have an offen-
sive flavor or aroma unless they have been neglected in field
dressing or allowed to sit around in the heat too long before
cooking. This "gamey" taste either comes from inattention
or improper cooking and is not a characteristic of wild animals in general. In fact I defy the average person to differentiate between wild turkey and domestic turkey if a piece
of each were put on a plate before him.

While discussing rabbits, squirrels, woodchucks, and the
others, it might be well to give one good, simple recipe for
preparing this kind of meat. Merely clean the animal thoroughly, cut up into the usual pieces, wash, and put into the
refrigerator for a day or two. It is better if it is not put in
the freezing compartment or the deep freeze unless you in-
tend to hold it for more than two or three days.

Then without any previous soaking, parboiling, or any
other treatment, dust each piece thoroughly with flour. This
can be done easily by putting some flour in a paper sack,
and then shaking each piece around in it with the top held
shut. Have a frying pan without a lid good and hot with
butter or oleo in it, and brown the pieces for ten or fifteen
minutes or until each is well crusted over the outside. Then
remove the pieces, put them in a roaster, add two-thirds to
three-quarters of a cup of water, put the lid on and set it in
the oven. Start at about 350° and reduce to 325° after

twenty minutes to a half hour. Young animals should be tender in an hour or a little more; older animals may take up to two hours.

Cooking the turkey is a relatively simple job. Stuff it if you like, put the giblets inside with the stuffing, and then rub the outside well with butter. Wrap entirely with aluminum foil and make as air tight and drip proof as possible. Then put in a roaster without a lid, and roast at 350° until tender. Generally it requires 18 to 25 minutes per pound of dressed bird, and the smaller the bird the longer the time required per pound. Also, an older bird will require more cooking than a young one. It is better to be overroasted and falling away from the bone than underdone and tough.

Many variations for roasting turkeys can be found and any recipes for domestic birds can be applied to the wild ones as well. But the surest way to ruin the rich natural flavor of the wild turkey is to fill it full of all kinds of junk, season it to high heaven, and pour a bottle of wine over it. The fancy recipes are for fancy people, not for me.

One delightful variation for cooking the wild turkey, in case you get tired of roast wild turkey all the time (who gets that many?), is to quick-fry the breast meat. When the turkey is still uncooked, remove the meat from each side of the breast in one large fillet. Then lay each piece of white meat on a table or board skin side down, and carefully cut thin steaks about one-third inch thick. Salt the pieces, let them stand a few minutes in a pile, and when good and moist dust each with flour. Shake off excess and drop in a sizzling frying pan of hot butter or oleo. Brown quickly on one side, flop them over and brown the other side. This should only take a very few minutes, and the meat should not be overcooked. Fry it fast like you would a good steak, and it will almost melt in your mouth. The meat will be juicy and delicious, and bear little resemblance to the same meat when roasted. This frying method applies equally as well to the breasts of grouse and pheasants.

# REFERENCES

Audubon, J. J. 1831. Ornithological Biography. (Edinburgh, A. Black), Vol. I. 512 pp.

Bailey, R. Wayne, Hans G. Uhlig, and George Breiding. 1951. Wild Turkey Management In West Virginia. Bulletin 2. West Virginia Conservation Commission, Charleston. 49 pp.

Blakey, H. L. 1937. The Wild Turkey On The Missouri Ozark Range. U. S. Biological Survey, Wildlife Research and Management Leaflet BS-77.

Dalke, Paul D., A. Starker Leopold, and David L. Spencer. 1946. The Ecology And Management Of The Wild Turkey In Missouri. Technical Bulletin 1. Missouri Conservation Commission, Jefferson City.

Davis, Henry E. 1949. The American Wild Turkey. Small-Arms Technical Publishing Company, Georgetown, S. C. 328 pp.

Gerstell, Richard and W. H. Long. 1939. Physiological Variations In Wild Turkeys And Their Significance In Management. Research Bulletin 2. Pennsylvania Game Commission, Harrisburg.

Leopold, A. Starker. 1943. The Molts Of Young Wild And Domestic Turkeys. Condor 45:133-145.

Leopold, A. Starker. 1944. The Nature Of Heritable Wildness In Turkeys. Auk 46(4):133-197.

Ligon, J. Stokley. 1946. History And Management Of Merriam's Wild Turkey. New Mexico Game and Fish Commission, Sante Fe. 84 pp.

McIlhenny, E. A. 1914. The Wild Turkey And Its Hunting. Doubleday-Page and Company, New York. 245 pp.

Mosby, H. S. and C. O. Handley. 1943. The Wild Turkey In Virginia. Commission of Game and Inland Fisheries, Richmond. 281 pp.

Wheeler, Robert J., Jr. 1948. The Wild Turkey In Alabama. Alabama Department of Conservation, Montgomery. 92 pp.